Pelican Books
The Creative Use of Calculat

J. P. Killingbeck received his B.Sc. in 1960 and his Ph.D. in 1963 both from the University of Nottingham. He then spent two years as a research fellow at the University of Toronto. On his return to England he joined the staff at the University of Hull, where he was appointed Reader in Theoretical Physics in 1980. In 1979 he was awarded a D.Sc. by the University of Nottingham. His other books are *Mathematical Techniques and Physical Applications* (with G. H. A. Cole) and *Techniques of Applied Quantum Mechanics*.

J. P. Killingbeck

THE CREATIVE USE OF CALCULATORS

Penguin Books

Penguin Books Ltd, Harmondsworth, Middlesex, England
Penguin Books, 625 Madison Avenue, New York, New York 10022, U.S.A.
Penguin Books Australia Ltd, Ringwood, Victoria, Australia
Penguin Books Canada Ltd, 2801 John Street, Markham, Ontario, Canada L3R 1B4
Penguin Books (N.Z.) Ltd, 182–190 Wairau Road, Auckland 10, New Zealand

First published 1981

Copyright © J. P. Killingbeck, 1981

Made and printed in Great Britain by
Richard Clay (The Chaucer Press) Ltd, Bungay, Suffolk
Set in 'Monophoto' Times

Contents

Introduction

The four-function calculator, which could *only* add, subtract, multiply and divide, is already a comparative rarity, and most machines nowadays can work out square roots, reciprocals, etc., and keep one or more numbers in a memory. In other words the 'power per pound' of calculators (both in terms of money and of weight) has increased considerably in recent years, and this would have been true even if the cash price had not been falling. All this makes available to us a calculating power and speed which was previously unattainable by most people.

Mechanical calculators have been in existence for over fifty years and electronic computers for about thirty, but they have in the main been used by specialists of one kind or another in business, government and universities. In so far as early large-scale electronic computers made an impression on the general public, it was often an unfavourable one – 'final demands' for £000.00, for example, and other follies connected with bank statements, vehicle registration and so on. Of course, a computer is controlled by its program, which is designed by men, and this fact is brought home to anyone who designs calculations even for a pocket calculator, as I encourage the reader to do throughout this book. A computer (or calculator) executes its calculations quite logically with infinite patience, in accord with its instructions and with its own internal structure. Although the present book is not about large-scale digital computers, it will become clear to the reader that even with a pocket calculator we must be careful to translate our intentions into unambiguous instructions which the calculator can execute. In a sense, then, a calculator *forces* its owner to think logically. This is partly why I take issue with those who regard the pocket calculator as a 'bad thing'. People who take this view usually hold that children will somehow become lazy or not learn mathematics properly if they can rely on the calculator to do their sums for them. What the fuss is about, actually, is *arithmetic*, not mathematics as it is understood by anyone of reasonable learning. Suppose that some-one asks, 'What is four plus two times three?' We need first to know some mathematical notation to be able to write down the symbols 4, 2 and 3 for the numbers mentioned. If we then just put the list of instructions [[4 + 2 × 3 =]]* into a selection of pocket calcu-lators, some will give the answer 18, while others will give the answer 10. There is a question of *mathematical* understanding and interpretation as to whether we should write the problem as $(4+2) \times 3$, or $4+(2 \times 3)$, whereas the *arithmetic* part involves remembering that $4 + 2 = 6$, and so on. I hope that point is clear: to use a calculator you have to understand what you are doing.

If there is any problem about children 'not knowing their tables' in schools today, it is not due to electronic calculators; it is more probably due to teachers who think that it is somehow harmful to induce children to learn *anything*.

I would have thought that pressing keys to see that $3 \times 7 = 21$ (in red numbers) would serve to re-inforce seeing it on a card or a wall-chart. Indeed, with the calculator a pupil can quickly be shown how to test pairs such as 3×7 and 7×3 to see that they both give 21, or that, in mathematical jargon, multiplication is commutative. To pick out such 'laws' on a static chart would be a more laborious process. In general a calculator allows many specimen calculations of a given kind to be performed in the same time as it would take to write out and perform one calculation on paper. An American proponent of finger-calculating, as it is taught in some American schools, asserts that a calculator will show that $3 \times 7 = 21$, but not that 3×7 means 'adding seven threes', in other words that multiplication is derived from addition. Well, on a modern calculator, if you press the keys [[3 +]] (and on some machines the constant key) and then repeatedly press the [[=]] key, you will see the result building up to the answer 21 after six additions. If the children who learn finger arithmetic are allowed the guidance of a teacher, presumably we can assume the same for children using a calculator! Further, at the stage when the child *has* the under-

---

* Throughout the book key stroke sequences are enclosed in end brackets [[and]]. The resulting display number is shown in a box.

standing, but just wants the answer, the calculator's speed at doing chains of calculations is obviously of practical use. It is my contention that, if used intelligently by a teacher, the electronic calculator can help in developing a deeper understanding both of arithmetic in particular and of mathematics in general. The same applies, of course, for the reader who is teaching himself.

One cannot avoid thinking by using a calculator, but one *can* be stimulated to think more critically about mathematical processes if one's use of the calculator is properly guided. As a simple example, we can spend more time learning *why* numbers are squared and added together in statistics if we can use a calculator to save time on the actual numerical work. Furthermore, we can learn a little mathematics in the process of summing the squares, as we shall see. In most universities it is now possible for a student to use his own pocket calculator in examinations, since most lecturers agree that it is the understanding of mathematical processes, the *use* of numbers, which examinations should test. Once you know *which* calculation to do, and *how* to do it, the speediest way to get the answer is the obvious one to use. My own interest in pocket calculators has extended over five years or so, during which time I have been an advocate of what might be called 'small science' – developing calculator methods (especially for problems in physics) which give results comparable to those from expensive large-scale computers. In this book I hope to communicate my view that pocket calculators can make a great contribution to the creative teaching and learning of mathematics. I have tried to set out in outline what *can* be done, and any creative teacher will quickly be able to think of ways of doing the job which seem better than mine. My work is intended mainly to stimulate ideas in the reader; in particular, it may help the general reader (who probably has not bothered much with mathematics since school, but may use a low-priced calculator for household calculations) to discover some of the fascination of mathematics. 'Playing about with numbers' has always been a way in which people have developed an interest in mathematics, and modern pocket calculators give unbounded scope for this.

There are three levels on which the book can be read. First, it tells the reader about modern calculators, and explains how to do a selection of practical calculations. Second, it shows how the practical problems can be used to lead on to various parts of mathematics. (For example, if we examine how best to evaluate sums of products of numbers, such as $(2 \times 3) + (4 \times 5)$, we naturally tend to ask when we need them, and this leads to elementary ideas about complex numbers and matrices.) Third, readers of the book will actually receive a slight conditioning towards certain ways of thinking which will be useful if they go on to study advanced mathematics. (For example, the repeated use of powers of numbers close to one is related to the idea of studying a Lie group by looking at elements close to the identity element.) Since much of the book is about calculators, the reader will get most out of it by having a calculator on hand to try out the methods which are described. The old saying that 'to learn mathematics you must *do* it' is particularly relevant here. At the end of each chapter are a few exercises, which encourage readers to consolidate their knowledge of the methods and ideas treated in the text. Solutions are presented with the exercises, since readers often find it irksome to keep turning to the back of a book. Those who wish to cheat by looking at the solutions may do so; it does not matter all that much provided they learn something!

I would like to thank my wife for playing the role of an 'average reader' as she laboured through successive versions of the manuscript (an iterative process, indeed!). My children unwittingly contributed a number joke which developed into section 4.17, one of the most creative bits in the book. David Nelson of Ampleforth College read the manuscript carefully and made many valuable comments. Finally, I would like to mention Professor L. F. Bates, who, in his role as an advisory editor of the journal *Contemporary Physics*, first gave me the stimulus to write down systematically my ideas about calculators; neither he nor I could have guessed how that beginning would lead to a new and interesting phase of my creative work. It was with regret that I learned of his death while this book was being completed.

July 1981

Physics Department
University of Hull

Chapter 1
General Calculator Design Features

1.1. Decimals and exponents

Before describing some of the capabilities of modern pocket calculators we must first deal with one mathematical preliminary which must be understood by the reader before he can follow any discussion about calculators. This is the concept of decimal notation, or the use of powers of numbers in general. There is at least one calculator (the Casio AL 10) which deals with fractions such as $\frac{1}{2}$ and $\frac{1}{4}$ directly, but for the most part anyone working with a calculator must become familiar with decimal notation (and can actually learn about it by using a calculator).

Consider the result of multiplying 5 by 5: $5 \times 5 = 25$. One shorthand way of writing 5×5 is as follows: $5 \times 5 = 5^2$. The number 2, called the *exponent*, reminds us how many times we must write down 5 in the product. Now consider the following pair of calculations, an addition and a multiplication:

$$2 + 1 = 3$$
$$25 \times 5 = 125.$$

In terms of our exponent notation, 25 is 5^2 and 5 is 5^1, while 125 is 5^3 (that is, $5 \times 5 \times 5$). The two equations show us that to multiply together 'powers of 5' such as 5^1 or 5^2 we can simply *add* the exponent numbers. Thus

$$5^2 \times 5^1 = 5^{(2+1)} = 5^3.$$

(Anyone familiar with school mathematics will remember that this 'law of exponents' is the essential one involved in the definition of logarithms.) Now, this law of adding exponents to describe multiplication is so simple that scientists use it as a basic convention and actually design the symbols for numbers so that the simple law always works! For example, what can we make of the symbols

5^0, 5^{-1} and $5^{\frac{1}{2}}$? Well, let us just automatically apply the idea of adding exponents and see what happens! If we try the equations

$$3+0 = 3$$
$$5^3 \times 5^0 = 5^3$$

(or these equations with any number instead of 3), it is clear that 5^0 must mean 1, since it leaves numbers unchanged when it *multiplies* them, just as 0 leaves numbers unchanged when it is *added* to them. Using now only the product equations, we can see from the products

$$5^{-1} \times 5^1 = 5^0 = 1$$
$$5^{\frac{1}{2}} \times 5^{\frac{1}{2}} = 5^1 = 5$$

that 5^{-1} is the reciprocal of 5 (i.e., $\frac{1}{5}$) since it gives 1 when multiplied by 5, while similarly $5^{\frac{1}{2}}$ denotes 'the square root of 5', $\sqrt{5}$, the number (actually approximately 2.236) which gives 5 when it is multiplied by itself.

Consider now the number twenty-seven, usually written 27. We know that in the exponent notation 10 is 10^1 and 1 is 10^0, so that 27, broken up into tens and units, becomes

$$27 = (2 \times 10^1) + (7 \times 10^0).$$

If we chose to count in fives instead of tens, and used powers of five, we could instead break 27 up into parts as follows, with the powers of 5 in descending order:

$$27 = (1 \times 25) + (0 \times 5) + (2 \times 1)$$
$$= (1 \times 5^2) + (0 \times 5^1) + (2 \times 5^0).$$

(Note that the 0 must be included so that each power is mentioned in the list.) By analogy with the 'tens' case, we pick out the first numbers in each bracket and denote our result as follows, in a special 'shorthand' symbolism:

$$(27)_{10} = (102)_5.$$

We say that 27 has been expressed in the *base* 5. In computer theory, numbers are often expressed in terms of base 2 (the binary system) or base 8 (the octal system). In everyday work, of course, we do not bother to put the small 10 subscript on 27, but only use such a special label when we take the extraordinary step of *not* using base 10.

All right then, but what about the number 2.236, which appeared in the above discussion as an approximation to the square root of 5? Well, we can see now that the symbol 10^{-1} means $\frac{1}{10}$; also 10^{-2} means $\frac{1}{100}$, that is 1 divided by 10^2 (or 100). The number 2.236 can then be broken up as follows:

$$(2 \times 10^0) + (2 \times 10^{-1}) + (3 \times 10^{-2}) + (6 \times 10^{-3}).$$

We see that the dot (the decimal point) tells us where to put the 'join' at which the negative powers of 10 start. If you enter 2.236 into a calculator and multiply by 10 you will see how the decimal point (the join) moves along one place to produce the answer 22.36. Since the introduction of decimal coinage in Britain the decimal notation has been used (perhaps unconsciously) by the general public. A few 'hybrid' symbols do appear, however; for example, if an object is priced at one pound and $15\frac{1}{2}$ pence, it is often written as £1.15$\frac{1}{2}$, whereas in our strict decimal notation it should be £1.155. On the other hand, if a petrol station advertises fuel at 127.9 pence (i.e., £1.279) per gallon, we have another problem, since we can only use half pence as our smallest unit of payment. (You could, of course, hand over a pound note and demand 0.7818608 gallons! I wonder if many readers have noted the 'psychological' prices such as £1.99, £2.99, which seem to fill certain shops; it is certainly worth 1p not to have one's intelligence insulted!) A recent correspondence in the *Guardian* newspaper shows that there is an interesting kind of confusion which the decimal notation causes for many people. They think of the decimal point as a separating mark between the pounds and pence, and so regard £1.9 as meaning 'one pound and nine pence', instead of 'one pound and ninety pence'. The use of the 'full' symbols £1.90 and £1.09 would make this distinction clear. Any reader who is still a little unsure about decimals can get the feel of them by remembering that 25p is a quarter of a pound, while working out $1 \div 4$ on a calculator gives 0.25 (twenty-five hundredths). Similarly $\frac{1}{8}$ is 0.125 (one hundred and twenty-five thousands), and so on.

When numbers are quoted in decimal notation it is common to speak of the number of *significant figures* or of *decimal places* which are quoted. Thus, the number 1.482 is given to four significant figures and to three decimal places, whereas 0.012 is given to two significant figures (since initial zeros are not counted) and to three decimal places. There is a common scientific convention by which 1.482, particularly if it refers to a measured quantity such as a length, is taken to mean 'nearer to 1.482 than to 1.481 or 1.483', that is, 'between 1.4815 and 1.4825'. If we write 1.482 as 1.4820, it is then taken to mean the more precise 'between 1.48195 and 1.48205'. If we are lazy, however, we often informally forget this convention and write 1.5 for $\frac{3}{2}$, rather than 1.500. For example, we used the lazy convention when we wrote 1.4815 in the preceding example! Incidentally, in some continental writings, particularly in scientific works, a comma is used for the decimal point (e.g., 1.2 becomes 1,2), while a dot means 'times' (e.g., 1.2 means 1×2).

We shall return again to some of the topics which arose in the preceding discussion, but will now proceed with our survey of basic calculator facilities.

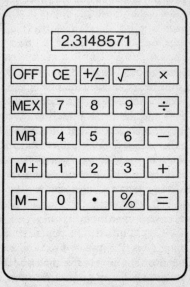

A typical simple calculator keyboard

1.2. Algebraic logic

The majority of calculators, particularly the lower-priced ones, use what is called *algebraic logic*, which we can illustrate by means of an example. To work out $4+2 = 6$, and then $6 \times 3 = 18$, we press the keys as follows:

$$[\![4\ +\ 2\ \times\ 3\ =]\!]\quad \boxed{18}\ .$$

The 18 (which we write in a square box) is the answer which appears in the display. Perhaps the name *simple* algebraic logic should be used, since some calculators (particularly those made by Texas Instruments) use a different system. A.O.S. (Algebraic Operating System). A calculator using A.O.S. would give the result

$$[\![4\ +\ 2\ \times\ 3\ =]\!]\quad \boxed{10}$$

since it has a built-in 'sense of priorities' which makes it work out products before sums. If we use the letters S.A.L. for simple algebraic logic, we can show the different ways the systems work as follows:

(S.A.L.) $(4+2) \times 3 = 6 \times 3 = 18$
(A.O.S.) $4+(2 \times 3) = 4+6 = 10.$

Clearly, it is no use saying 'That's not what I meant' when a silly answer comes out! You, the operator, have to check how the calculator interprets your instructions. Even if you have lost the handbook (or if it is not easy to understand), you can easily think up a few test calculations of the type used here and then make a record of the results. In general, it is always a good idea to make careful notes of the characteristics of a new calculator, since the maker's handbook may not say much about the knotty points which occur in your own pet calculations.

   Suppose that we require 'twice the square root of three'. In S.A.L. we have to use the keys as follows:

(S.A.L.) $[\![3\ \sqrt{}\ \times\ 2\ =]\!]\quad \boxed{3.4641}$

whereas in A.O.S we do not need to worry about taking the square root first:

(A.O.S.) $[\![2\ \times\ 3\ \sqrt{}\ =]\!]\quad \boxed{3.4641}\ .$

If we try the A.O.S. steps in an S.A.L. machine we get $2 \times 3 = 6$ first, and then take a square root. This produces $\sqrt{6}$ instead. In A.O.S., the system of priorities is such as to take the square root before doing the multiplication. In both cases, however, we note that to get $\sqrt{3}$ we *first* put in the 3, and *then* tell the calculator what to do to it (take its square root). Another example is the evaluation of $\sqrt{2} + \sqrt{3}$. We have

(A.O.S.) $[\![2 \ \sqrt{} \ + \ 3 \ \sqrt{} \ =]\!]$ $\boxed{3.1462}$

whereas on most S.A.L. machines we would probably have to work out the square roots separately and then add them (needing a memory of some kind). Note that in either form of algebraic logic we only need to press the $[\![=]\!]$ key once, to get the final answer. However, the answers at each intermediate stage *can* be seen if the operator watches the display carefully. Some of the calculators produced by the Texas Instruments company use a sophisticated A.O.S. which incorporates scientific functions such as cos x, exp x in its order of priorities. Some of the calculators made by the Casio company use a kind of partial A.O.S. (e.g., A.O.S. for the sum of square roots and for scientific functions, but S.A.L. for calculations such as $4 + 2 \times 3$); the low-priced Diplomat RS 1000 calculator sold by some supermarkets also has this feature.

In order to make clear what the calculator does to the numbers brackets have been used in our discussion. For example, when we write $(4 + 2) \times 3$ we mean that the $4 + 2$ inside the bracket is to be worked out to give one number, namely 6, which is then multiplied by 3. This use of logical brackets not only helps us to describe the calculation, it can actually be *used* on various calculators (e.g., the CBM 899D) which have bracket keys $[\![( ]\!]$ and $[\![ )]\!]$. Accordingly, we can get by with a minimum of re-arrangement of the calculation if we have a bracket facility – for instance, on the CBM 899D we get twice root three by pressing the keys $[\![2 \ \times \ (\ 3 \ \sqrt{} \ ) \ =]\!]$. (However, the 2 actually goes into the memory of the calculator during part of the calculation, so that the memory becomes inoperative for any other purpose.)

Clearly, then, you must try a few test calculations to see which particular variant of algebraic logic your calculator uses. The most general principle to remember is that the equals key completes a calculation 'up to date'. For example, even on an A.O.S. machine the key sequence

$[\![4 + 2 = \times 3 =]\!]$ $\boxed{18}$

will give the S.A.L. answer, since the first $[\![=]\!]$ completes the sum and starts afresh from there. In an S.A.L. machine the 6 appears in the display as the running total when the $[\![\times]\!]$ key is pressed in the sequence $[\![4 + 2 \times 3]\!]$, so we do not need to 'punctuate' the calculation with $[\![=]\!]$ key strokes.

1.3. Reverse Polish logic

A casual inspection of some calculators (e.g., some of those made by Hewlett-Packard, Prinztronic or Sinclair) will show that they have no $[\![=]\!]$ key. That does not mean that we cannot find the answer, but merely that the machine produces it internally once it has been told *what* to do. Most machines without an $[\![=]\!]$ key use *reverse Polish logic*. To work out $(4+2) \times 3$ we must use a key called the ENTER key (or whatever the manufacturer calls it for his particular calculator). We press the keys as follows:

$[\![4 \text{ ENT } 2 + 3 \times]\!]$ $\boxed{18}$

and the answer 18 appears; to get $4+(2 \times 3)$ we can use the steps

$[\![4 \text{ ENT } 2 \text{ ENT } 3 \times +]\!]$ $\boxed{10}$

and the answer 10 appears. Why is this so? Well, machines which use reverse Polish logic have an operating stack or arithmetic stack (as well as some separate memory stores). The layout below illustrates this; we show four levels in the stack, which is what many machines have. The $[\![\text{ENT}]\!]$ key has the effect of moving the contents of the stack 'up' by one level, with the contents of the top level 'dropping off the end' (to their death, alas!). Most calculator handbooks refer to motion up and down the stack, but it gives us the same results to draw the stack horizontally, so that 'up' becomes 'to the right'. Then we can show the second calculation above, the evaluation of $4+(2 \times 3)$, as follows, starting from an empty stack:

⟦4⟧	4		
⟦ENT⟧	4	4	
⟦2⟧	2	4	
⟦ENT⟧	2	2	4
⟦3⟧	3	2	4
⟦×⟧	6	4	
⟦+⟧	10		

(At all times only the extreme left-hand number appears in the display.)

We can see that the instruction × makes the calculator multiply together the two end numbers, while destroying the second number and moving everything one step to the left. The preceding example illustrates the main features of the reverse Polish system, so called because it is the reverse (operator last) form of the system (operator first) devised by the Polish logician Jan Lucasiewicz. As we have noted, most inexpensive calculators use some form of algebraic logic, since the makers of calculators have quite clearly decided that this is more easy for the general public to understand. There are still some scientists who strongly support the reverse Polish system as being more flexible; an author in the British journal *Keyboard* who recently implied that reverse Polish was on the way out provoked a letter of complaint from an indignant engineer in the next issue. For completeness we should note that some of the older types of bench calculator, such as the Toshiba BC-0802 and the Sharp ELSI 815S, use a system called *arithmetic logic*, which differs from S.A.L. in the treatment of subtraction. We do not mention this any further, since it does not appear on currently available pocket calculators. Calculators using arithmetic logic have a distinctive key marked ⁺₌, 'plus-equals'.

1.4. Arithmetic facilities

A few years ago many of the low-priced calculators available were four-function calculators, which could only perform the four standard operations $+ - \times \div$ of ordinary arithmetic. A check of a list of nineteen general-purpose calculators currently available from one nation-wide store shows that sixteen of them have some kind of memory facility, while ten of them have a square root key. Seventeen of them have a K constant operation (which we describe below), five have a reciprocal key and four have a squaring key. To the uninitiated, it may seem that the last two facts are a little surprising, but in fact reciprocal and squaring keys are not really necessary if the calculator has an automatic K constant operation. In the older types of calculator a K constant key was provided, which would retain a number so that it could be used in a series of simple calculations. For example, to find the circumferences of several circles we could retain 2π and multiply it in turn by the radii of the circles. The modern automatic K constant operation (as shown by the Litronix 2230, the CBM 899D and Diplomat RS 1000, to name but a few) involves no special key. To evaluate 3×5, for example, we simply use the key strokes $[\![3 \times 5 =]\!]$. However, the $[\![\times 5]\!]$ instruction is 'held' by the calculator, and pressing the $[\![=]\!]$ key a second time gives $(3 \times 5) \times 5$, or 3×5^2. Pressing the $[\![=]\!]$ key again gives 3×5^3, and so on. If we use the key strokes $[\![3 \times =]\!]$ we get 3^2, the square of 3. We have only given the calculator one number (3), so it uses $[\![\times 3]\!]$ as the 'held' operation. (To see that this is so, press the $[\![=]\!]$ key again, giving the answer 27, i.e., $3 \times 3 \times 3$.) A similar principle applies when the calculation involves, $+$, $-$ or $\div$ instead of $\times$; for example, to find 3×5^{-2} we use the strokes $[\![3 \div 5 = =]\!]$, and to get 5^{-1}, the reciprocal of 5, we use the strokes $[\![5 \div = =]\!]$. This last process works as follows: pressing the $[\![=]\!]$ key once divides 5 by 5, giving 1 in the display; pressing it again divides the 1 by the 5 again, yielding 0.2, i.e., $\frac{1}{5}$. If we work out 3×5, as in the previous example, and then want 2×5, 7×5, etc., we simply use the key strokes $[\![2 =]\!]$ and $[\![7 =]\!]$. The answers appear directly, since the $[\![\times 5]\!]$ instruction is held in the machine. As another example, to work out 8 per cent V.A.T. on a list of items it is easy to keep the $[\![\times 0.08]\!]$

as the held instruction, feed in a price and press the $[\![=]\!]$ key to get 8 per cent of it.

While the *automatic* K constant facility is speedier, the manual K constant (e.g., on the T.I.33) will give similar results. On the T.I.33 and similar machines the operator must press a special key marked $[\![K]\!]$ to tell the machine when to hold a number (or operation) as the constant quantity (e.g., $[\![20 \div K = =]\!]$ gives 0.05, the reciprocal of 20). All our automatic K constant programs can be converted for such machines by using the explicit $[\![K]\!]$ key stroke at the appropriate steps. Even an experienced operator sometimes finds it difficult to tell whether a calculator has an automatic K constant operation just by looking at the examples given in a handbook, and even then he is likely to be suspicious, not about what is *in* the handbook, but rather about what is conspicuously absent from it! All kinds of short cuts are possible with the automatic K constant facility, as we shall see in later chapters, but here is one simple example. Suppose we wish to calculate $(1.231)^8$, that is, multiply 1.231 by itself seven times. This can be done by entering 1.231, pressing the $[\![\times]\!]$ key, and then pressing the $[\![=]\!]$ key seven times (not eight times; remember the 'telegraph pole' problem from your schooldays). However, there is an alternative route to the answer. The key strokes $[\![1.231 \times =]\!]$ produce $(1.231)^2$; if we now use the key strokes $[\![\times =]\!]$, we get the square of $(1.231)^2$, that is $(1.231)^4$. Pressing the $[\![\times =]\!]$ keys again gives us the square of $(1.231)^4$, which is $(1.231)^8$ as we required. On some calculators (e.g., the Litronix 2230) the result can be obtained using only the key strokes $[\![1.231 \times \times \times]\!]$. If you have a simple calculator, try these key sequences on it and see what happens. It often happens that the owners of calculators are habitually using only a small part of the power which would be available to them if they really understood their machines. Of course, the theme of this book is that, even when you *do* understand your calculator, you can get even *more* out of it by using your head as well; the human head is another instrument not always used to its full capacity!

Working with calculators involves developing a kind of flexibility of thought, in which we see familiar formulae in a new light. For example, although x^2 is the same as 'x times x' by definition, we find it much easier to find $(5.71233)^2$ by some calculator process which does not involve entering the long number 5.71233 into the calculator twice. (This is where the automatic K constant is useful.) Also, if we want to work out, say, $(x+1) \times (x-1)$ for some x, we would have to enter x twice if we took the expression as it stands. In terms of abstract algebra $(x+1) \times (x-1)$ is the same as $x^2 - 1$, but to work out this latter expression needs only one entry of x if we have a squaring operation on the calculator. In other words, expressions which are 'abstractly' equivalent may not be equally convenient in practice when we use them on a calculator. Exercise 11 at the end of the chapter gives another simple example of this.

1.5. Memory facilities

The larger, more expensive calculators used by scientists often have many memories, each with its own number, so that it can be filled or emptied at will. Small pocket calculators usually make do with one memory, but there is quite a variety of ways in which the memory contents can be manipulated. The most simple machines have keys such as ⟦MS⟧ (memory store) and ⟦MR⟧ (memory recall), which simply put the displayed number into the memory or bring back the memorized number into the display. When ⟦MR⟧ operates it still keeps the memorized number in the memory, so that it can be recalled later if needed, but if a new number is put into the memory, using the ⟦MS⟧ key, the old memorized number is 'driven out' and replaced by the new one. There is usually also a ⟦MC⟧ key (memory clear) which replaces the memorized number by zero. Note that we do not say here that ⟦MC⟧ 'clears the memory', although that is what is usually said. If you press ⟦MR⟧ after ⟦MC⟧, you will see displayed the precise number zero – that is, 'zero' is in the memory, which is not the same as 'nothing' being in the memory. (If you think this is a logical quibble, turn your calculator on and press the keys ⟦+ 2 =⟧. You tell the calculator nothing about what you are adding 2 to, but it uses the definite number zero and gives the result 2.) The three keys mentioned above are fairly standard on calculators with memories. Two other memory keys possessed by some machines are the ⟦M+⟧ and ⟦M−⟧ keys. If there is a number in the display, pressing ⟦M+⟧ adds that number to the number in the memory, keeping the sum as the new contents of the memory. $[\![M -]\!]$ subtracts the display number from the memory. Finally, a useful key to have is a memory exchange key, $[\![ME]\!]$, which simply swaps the display number with the memory number. This process has the advantage that neither of the numbers is lost, whereas an $[\![MS]\!]$ key destroys the previous memory contents. With an $[\![ME]\!]$ key we can do the operations which the $[\![M +]\!]$ and $[\![M -]\!]$ keys would permit, although it takes a little longer. For example, if we have 2 in the memory and 3 in the display, we get 5 in the memory and keep 3 in the display if we press the $[\![M +]\!]$ key. Alternatively, we can get the same result by the key sequence $[\![ME + MR = ME]\!]$, as the reader should be able to work out.

It is the devising of alternative routes like this which helps a calculator owner to get a feel for his machine. On most modern calculators some of the keys are redundant, in the sense that we could, if necessary, perform their functions by using combinations of other keys. This leads to the idea of 'broken calculator' games, which are explained in a later chapter. Indeed, when calculators are getting very old it occasionally happens that one or two keys become worn and inoperative, so 'broken calculator' exercises are not necessarily of intellectual interest only. (In fairness I should add that the reliability of modern calculators has made this a rare occurrence.) While we are concentrating here mainly on simple calculators, it is worth noting that the more expensive calculators, particularly those used in statistical work, have a key which adds the square of the display number into the memory. Exercise 9 at the end of the chapter explains how to use the $[\![MS]\!]$ key to get the same effect as that of the automatic K constant facility.

1.6. Overflow and underflow. Scientific notation

The majority of inexpensive calculators can display eight figures, which means that the largest number they can show is 99999999. Suppose, then, that we give such a calculator the problem of working out the product $50,001 \times 3102$. What happens when we cause this overflow of the machine's capacity will depend on the particular calculator, but here are some typical cases. The C B M 899 D shows the display E 155510310, the E (error) sign warning us that some figures have been chopped off the right-hand end of the result. If we then divide by 10 the display number is unchanged, but the E vanishes, showing that *one* figure was missing at the end. The same product calculation on the Diplomat RS 1000 yields 15510310, but with a decimal point glowing between each figure to act as the error indicator. The correct result cannot be recovered in this case. The Litronix 2230 and the Rockwell 61R have what is sometimes called a *wraparound decimal* facility: when the result is too big, these calculators divide the result by 10^8 before displaying it. For our specimen product they would show the result 1.551031. In none of the above cases do we find out that the last figure of the product is a 2, although we can easily see that it must be by looking at the numbers to be multiplied. Overflow problems can occur in the middle of a calculation, and we should try to avoid this. For example, if we wanted to divide the product which we have just been discussing by 572, we could avoid the overflow process by doing the division first, that is, by using the result

$$\frac{50,001 \times 3102}{572} = \frac{50,001}{572} \times 3102.$$

To do the calculation on any modern calculator (of S.A.L. type) we then use the key strokes

$$[\![50001 \div 572 \times 3102 =]\!] \quad \boxed{271159.26}$$

and get the result (271159.26) without overflow problems. In principle there should be figures after the 6, but we can only get eight figures in the display. We say that the result has been *rounded* to eight figures, and in a long string of calculations the *rounding errors* caused by this effect may have to be considered carefully. There are some calculators which avoid (or diminish) the problem by having inside them more than eight figures while displaying only eight figures to the user. The operator can make tests to find out whether this is happening, but most manufacturers are proud enough to emphasize such a feature strongly in their handbook! One simple check which often works is to put in some number which fills the display, and then use the keys $[\![\times 25 \div 25 =]\!]$. If the calculator does not keep inside it more figures than it displays, you may not recover all of the original number. The opposite problem to overflow is underflow, which happens when a result is too small to be shown in the display. For example, dividing 1 by 10,000 and then further by 1000 would give 'point eight noughts one', but the 1 would be off the end of an eight-figure display and so a zero answer would be obtained.

In science it is often necessary to deal with very large or very small numbers. For example, the number of atoms in a small lump of metal is about 10^{23} (or 1 followed by 23 noughts), while the wavelength of yellow light in metres is about 6×10^{-7} (point six noughts six). To display such numbers it is necessary to use a calculator with *scientific notation*. In this notation the last three spaces in the display are used to show the exponent attached to the 10. Thus the number 123,450,000 would appear as

in scientific notation. The 08 tells us to use 10^8 as multiplying factor; there are *two* spaces for the exponent, so we can go up to 10^{99}. The middle space shows a minus sign in case we have a small number (such as the example 5×10^{-7}) which needs a negative exponent. Thus calculators with scientific notation can handle very large and very small numbers, so that overflow and underflow problems are not so likely to occur.

Although scientific notation is *not* found on most low-priced calculators, this does not mean that such calculators cannot handle big (or small) numbers. All we have to do is remember the law of exponents (described in section 1.1) and note that multiplying numbers together can be done in any order (in mathematical jargon, the multiplication of numbers is commutative). For example, we can break up a product of large numbers as follows:

$123,450,000 \times 789,123$

$= (1.2345 \times 10^8) \times (7.89123 \times 10^5)$

$= (1.2345 \times 7.89123) \times (10^8 \times 10^5)$

$= (1.2345 \times 7.89123) \times 10^{13}$

$= (9.7417234) \times 10^{13}.$

Here the calculator was used to work out only the product of
two small numbers, and we did the powers of 10 by mental arithmetic. Looking at the two small numbers we can see that the last
figure in their product should be 5 (because $3 \times 5 = 15$; 5 down,
1 to carry). This shows us that something is missing, and actually
the exact answer should be 9.741723435. We have here another
example of the rounding error discussed previously, which arises
when the calculator can only show eight figures. Anyone with
experience of decimals could see that there must be *two* figures
missing by using the following rule, which is an addition rule (like
that for exponents). We take the number 1.2345, and note that there
are four figures after the point. 7.89123 has five figures after the
point. *We add 5 to 4, giving 9, and this gives us the number of figures
after the point which we should have in the product*. As another
example of this rule, if we square the number 1.2345, we expect
to get a number with eight figures after the decimal point, whereas
an eight-figure calculator will give us 1.5239902. (What is the
missing figure?) In some calculators it is possible to set the display
so that it will only show a fixed number of figures after the decimal
point, but most calculators operate in *floating point notation*,
showing as much of the answer as they can (starting from the left,
of course!). A case where fixed-point operation might be useful is
in monetary calculations, which usually only need at most three
figures after the point in the final displayed results, since $\frac{1}{2}$p is £0.005
in decimal notation. Some calculators have a percentage key, so
that the user need not remember, for example, that 8 per cent is
0.08. With such a key we add 8 per cent V.A.T. to £3.41 as follows:
[3.41 + 8 % =]. This produces the answer 3.6828 (i.e., £3.68).

1.7. Miscellaneous features

Calculator chips are very small; most of the bulk of a calculator
is occupied by the number display system and the keyboard. The
keys are the obvious 'mechanical' parts of the machine which
might be expected to wear out more quickly than the electronic
parts. Different users (and manufacturers) have different views
about keys. Some prefer them to be 'stiff', so that a firm push
is needed to operate them, making accidental pushing or double-

pushing less likely. Others prefer sensitive keys which respond to a light touch. This makes for speedy operation after the user has got the feel of the keys, but anyone using one of these machines (e.g., some of the recent Casio models) will feel a little ham-handed if he is used to the stiffer keys. The Sharp EL 8130 calculator has no mechanical keys: a light touch on the appropriate square of the key panel acts as a 'key push', while a pinging sound indicates that the key has registered. The idea of 'keyless' calculators had been in the air for some time, so we can expect this development to be continued by various companies. Whether we use keys or not, it is quite easy to make a mistake when keying in numbers, and many calculators have a special $[\![CE]\!]$ (clear entry) key, which removes *only* the last entry. For example, suppose we try to enter the symbols $[\![3.311 \times 1.212]\!]$ and accidentally enter 1.1 as we start the second number. Pressing the $[\![CE]\!]$ key brings us back to the start of the second number but leaves all the preceding symbols unchanged. An ordinary clear key would destroy everything, so that we would have to start again at the first 3. Of course, with a little thought we can save the day without a $[\![CE]\!]$ key if we see the error in time. Thus, we could proceed as follows, using a division to remove the mistake:

$$[\![3.311 \times 1.1 \div 1.1 \times 1.212]\!].$$

This might seem a lot of fuss about nothing, but it is not! In a long calculation, the 3.311 may be the result of some complicated previous arithmetic. If this result has just appeared in the display and we have not written it down somewhere, we cannot afford to lose it while correcting the 1.212 entry because this might mean having to work it out again!

Some of the large calculators still use light-emitting diode (L.E.D.) number displays. Displays were almost always red in colour in the early days, but green digitrons are becoming more common and are kinder to the eye. Liquid crystal displays are widely used in small calculators, and should become even more popular in the next few years. Though their lifetime is not as great as that of L.E.D.s, they do give better visibility in bright lighting conditions and they require less power to operate. This last fact is the most important one, since it means that battery-operated calculators can work for long periods; for example, the CBM

L C 5 K I is claimed to give a battery life of 5000 hours, and battery lives of thousands of hours are quoted for various other calculators with liquid crystal displays. The life of an ordinary dry cell in an L.E.D. machine is often ten hours or less, although at present there are available both Ever Ready and Duracell special batteries for use in calculators. (The Duracell alkaline batteries are claimed to last up to four times as long as most ordinary cells.) Several companies are developing lithium-based batteries, which will give a much longer lifetime even in an L.E.D. calculator. Also likely to become increasingly common in the near future is the fluorescence-actuated display (F.L.A.D.), which uses about the same power as the liquid crystal display, but can give a range of colours between red and green. Rechargeable batteries, which are charged up using a mains unit, can be used with some calculators and give an operating cost per calculating hour which is much less than that of throw-away batteries. The cost ratio is roughly 100:1 for an L.E.D. machine (at current prices, if the reader will forgive the pun!). However, this kind of economic reasoning will lose its force as cheap liquid crystal calculators become widely available, or if current research on other low power-drain types of display proves fruitful. The Imperial 1981 calculator is an alternative attempt to solve the power problem, using a photocell as power source. The larger programmable types of calculator use quite a lot of power and are best kept in the same place (at home or in an office), using a mains transformer unit. There is one obvious way of losing battery power which almost every user discovers, and that is to leave the calculator accidentally turned on! Nowadays several companies (e.g., Litronix and C B M) incorporate an automatic off switch in some models, so that they turn themselves off if left unattended for a few minutes. The Prinztronic Program calculator replaces any displayed number by a row of decimal points after a few seconds, to cut down the display power required; the display can be restored by a single key stroke.

In later chapters there will be more to say about such things as dual-purpose keys, scientific function keys and so on. For the moment it is suggested that the reader should try (or at least read through) the following few exercises, which deal with typical features of a modern low-priced calculator.

Exercises

1. Write 1 pound 95½ pence in decimal notation. Using the automatic K constant facility, find the cost of 7 items, 15 items and 23 items at this price per item.

Solution

£1.955. ½p is five thousands of a pound, i.e., 0.005.

With an automatic K constant we need to use only the following few key strokes:

$$[\![7 \; \times \; 1.955 \; =]\!] \quad \boxed{13.685} \quad [\![15 \; =]\!] \quad \boxed{29.325} \quad [\![23 \; =]\!] \quad \boxed{44.965}.$$

Remember that $[\![\times \; 1.955]\!]$ is the operation 'held' in the calculator. There are some calculators which have a 'forwards' K constant facility, so that we have to use $[\![1.955 \; \times \; 7 \; =]\!]$ as the initial calculation.

2. Your calculator will have a 'sign change' key, marked $[\![CS]\!]$ or $[\![\pm]\!]$. This changes the sign of the display – for instance, to enter -5 you would use the key strokes $[\![5 \; \pm]\!]$. Suppose now that the ordinary subtraction key will not work, and that we want to work out $17-3$. What do we do?

Solution

$$17-3 = 17+(-3) = (-3)+17.$$

(Commutativity of addition as well as multiplication!)

We use the key strokes

$$[\![17 \; + \; 3 \; \pm \; =]\!] \quad \boxed{14}.$$

3. To convert kilograms to pounds we multiply by 2.2046, which we can call 2.2 to a very good approximation. Dividing a number by 10 in the decimal system involves moving the decimal point one place to the left. Use this idea *without* your calculator to convert 17.21 kilograms to pounds. To convert litres to gallons we multiply by 0.220; what is 17.21 litres in gallons?

Solution

$17.21 \times 2 = 34.42$ (Mental arithmetic!)
$17.21 \times 0.2 = 3.442$ (Move point one place to left)
$17.21 \times 2.2 = 37.862$ (Add the two previous results)
17.21 litres $= 3.7862$ gallons (Move point one place to left)

4. 1 inch equals 2.54 centimetres. How many square centimetres are there in 23.7 square inches? How many cubic centimetres are there in 17.9 cubic inches? How many metres are there in a foot?

Solution

$23.7 \times (2.54)^2 = 152.90292$
Key strokes $[\![23.7 \ \times \ 2.54 \ = \ =]\!]$

$17.9 \times (2.54)^3 = 293.32844$
Key strokes $[\![17.9 \ \times \ 2.54 \ = \ = \ =]\!]$

A metre is 100 centimetres. A foot is 12 inches, which equals $12 \times 2.54 = 30.48$ centimetres, which equals 0.3048 metres. (To divide by 100 we move the decimal point *two* places to the left.)

5. Given in the table are the amounts of tax payable by a married couple with two children under 12 (as proposed in the 1978 British Budget). The dot which separates pounds from pence acts exactly as a decimal point in calculator work.

	£	£	£	£
Income	2000	4000	6000	7000
Tax	66.25	702.60	1382.60	1722.60
Income	8000	9000	10,000	15,000
Tax	2062.60	2418.50	2831.75	5559.75

Consider a family with income of £6000. What percentage of this is paid in tax? What is the tax rate (in per cent) on the last £1000 of their income? Try the same calculation for an income of £15,000. Now suppose that the tax rate for incomes over £10,000 is raised to 100%. Imagine that after this tax change the company employing the £15,000 man drops his salary to £10,000. What do they save on their salaries bill? How much worse off is he? How much tax revenue is lost to the Exchequer?

Solution

At £6000, the fraction paid in tax is $(1382.6) \div (6000) = 0.230 = 23\%$. The figures in the table show that the rate is constant between £4000 and £7000 and equals $(1722.6 - 702.6) \div 3000 = 0.34 = 34\%$. At £15,000 the fraction paid in tax is 37.1%; we do not have the tax for £14,000, so cannot do the calculation exactly, but between £10,000 and £15,000 the average tax rate is 54.6%. The answers to the last part are £5000, £0, and £2728 or £5000, depending on how you do the calculation! Of course, the tax payer is worse off by £2272 than he was *before* the 100% tax, but this is not affected by the salary drop, and may be partly restored by indirect benefits.

6. Most simple calculators have the automatic K constant facility which is described in section 1.4. How could you use such a calculator as a comptometer? The traditional mechanical comptometer has a knob which adds one to the indicated number at each press, so that a count can be made of any collection which the observer is scanning by eye.

Solution

Use the keys ⟦CLR − 1 + 1 =⟧, then press ⟦=⟧ repeatedly to do the counting. This gives the following displays:

⟦CLR⟧	0	Clear sets display to zero.
⟦−⟧	0	Minus instruction stored.
⟦1⟧	1	Latest entry displayed. 0 and − stored.
⟦+⟧	−1	0−1 evaluated and displayed. + stored.
⟦1⟧	1	Latest entry displayed. −1 and + stored.
⟦=⟧	0	−1+1 = 0 displayed. +1 held as K constant operation.
⟦=⟧	1	0+1 = 1. First counting stroke.
⟦=⟧	2	1+1 = 2.

Note how using the ⟦=⟧ key keeps on repeating the K constant operation. At the step where ⟦+⟧ is pressed, we would bring into play a −1 K constant operation if we pressed ⟦=⟧ instead. Try it and see!

7. Converting a temperature of C degrees Centigrade into its equivalent Fahrenheit temperature F involves using the conversion formula:

$$F = \frac{9}{5} \times C + 32.$$

Taking as an example $C = 10$ degrees, show how F can be worked out on an S.A.L. calculator, an A.O.S. calculator and a reverse Polish calculator. By considering how to get back from F to C (that is, how to 'undo' the calculation) construct the formula which gives us C if we have F.

Solution

Although not essential, it is convenient to replace the fraction by its equivalent decimal number 1.8 (note that $\frac{9}{5} = \frac{18}{10} = 1.8$). Two common key stroke sequences for converting 10°C into Fahrenheit are as follows:

(*a*) $[1.8 \times 10 + 32 =]$ $\boxed{50}$ works with S.A.L. or A.O.S.
(*b*) $[32 + 10 \times 1.8 =]$ $\boxed{50}$ works only with A.O.S.

The use of (*b*) on an S.A.L. machine gives $(32 + 10) \times 1.8 = 75.6$, which is incorrect. If we retain 1.8 as $\frac{9}{5}$, then 10×1.8 becomes $10 \times 9 \div 5$; both sequences work equally well. An A.O.S. machine has an order of priorities which is described by the mnemonic word BODMAS: that is, Brackets, Of (e.g., square root of), Divide, Multiply, Add, Subtract. Thus, division precedes multiplication, so that an A.O.S. calculator behaves as follows:

$$10 \times 9 \div 5 = 10 \times (9 \div 5) = 10 \times 1.8 = 18$$
$$10 \div 5 \times 9 = (10 \div 5) \times 9 = 2 \times 9 = 18.$$

The same result is obtained in both cases.

On a reverse Polish machine there are many different ways of proceeding; indeed, it is this flexibility which makes some scientists prefer reverse Polish logic to algebraic logic. Two possible key stroke sequences are:

(*c*) $[10 \text{ ENT } 9 \times 5 \div 32 +]$
(*d*) $[32 \text{ ENT } 10 \text{ ENT } 9 \times 5 \div +].$

The stack arrangement for sequence (*c*) is as follows (the reader can treat sequence (*d*) similarly):

⟦10⟧	10			

⟦ENT⟧	10	10		

⟦9⟧	9	10		

⟦×⟧	90			

⟦5⟧	5	90		

⟦÷⟧	18			

⟦32⟧	32	18		

⟦+⟧	50			

It should be noted here that not all reverse Polish calculators behave in the same way as regards the last (right-hand end) store in the stack. If this store contains a number, on Hewlett-Packard machines it retains that number under downward (that is, leftward) operations, whereas on some other calculators the contents of the last register are lost. This 'stick to the ceiling' effect is useful if the number concerned is needed for later calculations.

The formula for getting C from F can be constructed easily by setting up a table as follows:

Doing (Down)	*Undoing (Up)*
Take C	Get C
Multiply by 1.8	Divide by 1.8
Add 32	Subtract 32
Get F	Take F
$F = (\frac{9}{5} \times C) + 32$	$C = \frac{5}{9} \times (F - 32)$

The 'undoing' process leads to the formula which gives C in terms of F. Of course, someone familiar with simple algebra would arrive at the formula for C very quickly, but only because he has learned to do mentally the steps which we set out explicitly in the table. This tabular approach is suggested by the need to devise a key stroke sequence to undo the results of some previous sequence, but it seems that students learning about mappings and their inverses find this approach helpful.

8. In section 1.2 we discuss the problem of evaluating $\sqrt{2} + \sqrt{3}$. Suppose you have an S.A.L. machine with a square root key but without a memory, and you don't want to write down any intermediate results. Can you see how to do the calculation?

Solution

The trick is to use the following result:

$$(\sqrt{2} + \sqrt{3})^2 = 2 + 3 + 2\sqrt{(2 \times 3)}.$$

We work out the right-hand side and then take its square root. The key strokes

$$[\![2 \times 3 = \sqrt{} \times 2 + 3 + 2 = \sqrt{}]\!]$$

will suffice on many S.A.L. calculators. (As an example of the many possible variations on the S.A.L. theme, note that the Litronix 2230 will give $\sqrt{2} + \sqrt{3}$ using the key strokes $[\![2 \sqrt{} + 3 \sqrt{} =]\!]$, even though it operates in the S.A.L. manner for simple arithmetic.)

Calculators without automatic K constant

It should be clear from the discussion so far that anyone buying a simple calculator should look for one with the automatic K constant facility. However, some readers will already have calculators *without* this facility, which makes some calculations more tedious. Here are a few exercises based on the examples in Chapter 1.

9. How can we use a calculator with one memory to do the same things which we did in section 1.4 with the automatic K constant? In particular how do we multiply a sequence of numbers by 5, and how do we find higher and higher powers of a given number?

Solution

To multiply the numbers 1.23, 3.91, etc., by 5 we use the key strokes

⟦1,23 × 5 MS =⟧   │ 6.15 │

⟦3.91 × MR =⟧   │ 19.55 │.

Note how the ⟦MS⟧ (memory store) puts the display number 5 into the memory. This feature is the same for all algebraic logic machines: a key stroke such as ⟦=⟧ or ⟦×⟧ or ⟦+⟧ instead of ⟦MS⟧ would make the calculator show 1.23×5 in the display, whereas an ⟦MS⟧ always uses the number *currently* in display with no reference to the rest of the pending calculation. Any reader who is unsure about this point can always put the 5 into the memory separately as follows:

⟦5 MS 1.23 × MR = 3.91 × MR =⟧.

To evaluate successive powers of 3.194, say, we can make × act like × =:

⟦3.194 MS × MR ×⟧   │ 10.201636 │

⟦MR =⟧   │ 32.584025 │

or if we have a squaring key ⟦x^2⟧ we can get the powers 2, 4, 8 and so on by repeated squaring. With *both* memory and a squaring key we can get, for example $(3.194)^7$ by using ⟦× MR =⟧ (6 times) *or* by using the key strokes

⟦3.194 MS x^2 x^2 x^2 ÷ MR =⟧   3391.1289

since we can use the law of indices (see section 1.1): $x^7 = x^8 \div x$. The reader can check that the second way to do the calculation uses twelve key strokes whereas the first way uses twenty-four.

The reader should now be able to translate all the automatic K constant key sequences in this book into a form involving ⟦MS⟧ and ⟦MR⟧ key strokes. For example, the solution to exercise 4 has the automatic K constant sequence

⟦17.9 × 2.54 = = =⟧

which becomes

⟦17.9 × 2.54 MS × MR × MR =⟧.

10. Suppose we have a reciprocal key on our S.A.L. calculator

(whereas we could get reciprocals on an automatic K constant machine by using $[\![\div = =]\!]$).

According to ordinary arithmetic it should be true that

$$\frac{2345}{6789} = (\text{reciprocal of } 6789) \times 2345.$$

Try it and see! Which of the two answers is the better one? (If you don't have a reciprocal key, work out $1 \div 6789$ directly.)

Solution

To work out the right-hand-side expression we use the strokes

$[\![6789 \; \tfrac{1}{x}]\!]$ ⟦0.0001472⟧ $[\![\times \; 2345 =]\!]$ ⟦0.345184⟧.

To work out the left-hand side we use the strokes

$[\![2345 \div 6789 =]\!]$ ⟦0.3454116⟧.

Multiplying the two results by 6789 shows that the second one gives a result much closer to 2345 and so is the better result. The reason is that the intermediate result 0.0001472 has lost three significant digits because of the three leading zeros. If we use 0.6789 instead of 6789 before taking the reciprocal we get

$[\![0.6789 \; \tfrac{1}{x}]\!]$ ⟦1.4729709⟧ $[\![\times \; 2345 =]\!]$ ⟦3454.1167⟧

and can move the decimal point along four places mentally when reading the answer. In the original calculation the leading zeros pushed the digits 9709 'off the end' and they were lost.

11. Using an S.A.L. calculator with one memory, how can we work out the product of $x+2$ and $x+4$ for some input number x, which we only enter once? Could we do it with no memory at all?

Solution

We note that $x+4$ is simply $(x+2)+2$. The key strokes

$[\![x + 2 = MS + 2 \times MR =]\!]$

will do the trick since they store $x+2$, work out $x+4$, and then multiply $(x+4)$ by $(x+2)$. If we have no memory we can use a trick which will be developed in more detail in later chapters. We do a little algebra as follows:

$$(x+2) \times (x+4) = x^2 + 6x + 8$$
$$= (x+3) \times (x+3) - 1$$
$$= (x+3)^2 - 1.$$

This shows us that the key strokes

$$[\![x \ + \ 3 \ = \ x^2 \ - \ 1 \ =]\!]$$

will do the calculation if we are able to work out the square of a number on the calculator.

12. Suppose that we work out $\sqrt{10}$ on two simple calculators and one gives 3.162277 while the other gives 3.162278. Which will be the better result?

Solution

A more accurate calculator would show that the result is 3.1622777... Most calculators *truncate* the result, i.e. just chop off any digits which they can't display. They thus give a result which is too low. However, some calculators use *scientific rounding*, i.e. they get as near as possible to the answer with their display. If the second calculator is of this type its higher result will necessarily be the better one. Low-priced calculators are almost invariably of the simple truncating type.

Some things to revise

In this chapter you should have found out something about calculators and should have learned three mathematical ideas:

1. The law of exponents (section 1.1).
2. The 'addition law' for the number of decimal places in a product (section 1.6).
3. The law of commutativity of multiplication (section 1.6). Make sure that you know these fairly well, since they will crop up in later chapters.

Chapter 2
Everyday Calculations on the Simple Calculator

2.1. Introduction

In this chapter we shall discuss in more detail how to use a calculator efficiently in various simple everyday calculations. When readers have gained confidence in their handling of the calculator they can then pass on to the next chapter, where we begin to explore various mathematical ideas with the aid of the calculator. In Chapter 4 we get on to the use of fully-fledged scientific calculators, but in this chapter and the next we stick to simple calculators, which we assume to have an automatic K constant facility, a square root key and a memory. The K constant facility is not *essential* if we have a memory (see exercises 9, 10 and 11 at the end of Chapter 1), but we do make frequent use of the square root key. *However, even readers with only the most basic four-function calculator should find much useful material in this chapter and throughout the book.* As has been explained previously, the intention is to get readers to use their heads as well as their calculators! First of all we must remember to pay our respects to a now-neglected friend.

2.2. What about logarithms?

Until quite recently the most usual way for a student to perform multiplication and division of numbers was to use a table of logarithms. Even engineers using a slide-rule were in effect using logarithms, since the distances along the slide-rule scale are proportional to the logarithms of numbers. The simple electronic calculator does multiplication and division quickly, and is usually very accurate (whereas log tables are usually called 'four-figure' or 'five-figure' to indicate the number of decimal places to which they are reliable). For the routine tasks of arithmetic, then, the simple calculator has rendered log tables obsolete. It is because of this that we must be careful not to dismiss logarithms too lightly, since they do have some valuable applications which do not hinge on their use to facilitate numerical calculations. In later chapters we shall look at some problems which involve logarithms; for the moment we shall consider how the idea of a logarithm is related to the idea of powers of numbers, which was discussed right at the start of the book in section 1.1. We shall be making extensive use of the square root key on the calculator.

If we put the number 10 into a simple calculator and keep on pressing the square root key, we get the following sequence of numbers (which the reader can check if he will 'sing along' with the author, using his own calculator):

Number	Power
10	1
3.162277	$\frac{1}{2}$
1.778279	$\frac{1}{4}$
1.333521	$\frac{1}{8}$
1.154782	$\frac{1}{16}$

In the column marked *Power* we have put down the power of 10 which is involved. For example, the notation explained in section 1.1 means that we must write $\sqrt{10}$ as $10^{\frac{1}{2}}$, and the square root of $10^{\frac{1}{2}}$ must be $10^{\frac{1}{4}}$, and so on. To get the idea of a logarithm we must turn the table back to front; instead of saying, '1.778279 is 10 to the power $\frac{1}{4}$,' we say, '$\frac{1}{4}$ is the log (to the base 10) of the number 1.778279.' If we look at the table and the way in which we constructed it, the following points naturally arise:

1. We could start with any positive number (e.g., 8 or 2 or 3.791) instead of 10 and proceed to get logs to base 8 (or 2 or 3.791) instead of base 10, although the base 10 is most often used in log tables designed to be used for multiplication and division. Using a negative number, however, would give us no results – the calculator refuses to play!

2. Although we have obtained only a few particular numbers in our table it is clear that the numbers decrease together down each column, so that we expect intuitively to be able to find numbers which 'fill in the gaps'. For example, we expect that $\log_{10}3$ (log

to the base 10 of 3) will be some number between $\frac{1}{4}$ and $\frac{1}{2}$. This is so, of course; the reader who has a table of logarithms to hand can check that it contains our specimen numbers and many more which fill in the gaps.

3. By using *only* the numbers in the table we can fill in some of the gaps with the aid of the calculator. Thus, if we remember the principles set out in section 1.1, in particular the exponent law for multiplication, we have the equation

$$10^{\frac{1}{4}} \times 10^{\frac{1}{8}} = 10^{(\frac{1}{4}+\frac{1}{8})} = 10^{\frac{3}{8}}$$
$$= 1.778279 \times 1.333521$$
$$= 2.371372$$

and so can put the numbers 2.371372 and $\frac{3}{8}$ into the table. We can get this result more quickly, however, by noting that $10^{\frac{3}{8}}$ is also equal to $(10^{\frac{1}{8}})^3$; on a calculator with automatic K constant we can work out $(10^{\frac{1}{8}})^3$ with the key strokes

$$[\![10 \ \sqrt{} \ \sqrt{} \ \sqrt{} \ \times \ = \ =]\!] \quad \boxed{2.371373}.$$

This differs by 1 in the last digit from our previous calculation. Why? Well, the calculator actually shows 1.7782792 for $10^{\frac{1}{4}}$ and 1.3335213 for $10^{\frac{1}{8}}$, whereas we wrote down the results only to the nearest six decimal places in the table. Going directly to the result by this sequence of key strokes does not involve such large *rounding errors* (also mentioned in section 1.6) and so gives a slightly better answer.

It should be clear from the discussion so far that the basic idea behind finding logs of numbers is to convert multiplication into addition and division into subtraction, by using the principle that the log of $(a \times b)$ equals $\log a + \log b$ while the log of $(a \div b)$ equals $\log a - \log b$. This is just a practical application of the law of exponents of section 1.1. For the example above the reasoning would run as follows, if we take the required logs from our table:

$$\log(1.778279) + \log(1.333521) = \frac{1}{4} + \frac{1}{8}$$
$$= \frac{3}{8}$$
$$= \log(2.371372).$$

Therefore,

$$1.778279 \times 1.333521 = 2.371372.$$

The result is accurate only to the six decimal places shown in our 'log tables', whereas the exact product of the two numbers on the left would have twelve digits after the decimal point.

Of course, to work out $a \times b$ we have to look up the logs of a and b, add them, and then look up the antilog of the sum – that is, we have to find the number which has $\log a + \log b$ as its logarithm. Thus, to use log tables we must translate into log language and then back again. It is this work which is avoided by using the electronic calculator; nevertheless it is amusing to note that most calculators still do precisely this translation for some calculations! Calculators with a $[\![y^x]\!]$ key will work out powers of numbers – for instance, $(23)^3$ – but they do this by working out $\log 23$, multiplying it by 3 and then taking the antilog. The only distinction between the calculator's procedure and that of the human operator is that the calculator uses logs to base e $(= 2.7182818)$ or base 2, instead of base 10, and that it does the calculation in a fraction of a second! On some calculators (e.g., the CBM SR 1800) the log of 23 is actually displayed when the $[\![y^x]\!]$ key is pressed in the key sequence $[\![23 \; y^x \; 3 \; =]\!]$. It is because of this use of logs that many calculators with a y^x powering key cannot work out powers of negative numbers, such as $(-23)^3$, since no positive or negative number can be found which is the log of a negative number. A demand for $(-23)^3$ produces an error signal, although a few advanced machines would display $(+23)^3$ as well as the error signal. Here is one of those rare cases in which the human operator is smarter than the machine, since he knows that

$$(-23)^3 = (23)^3 \times (-1)^3 = -12167,$$

whereas it requires a fairly clever program to make a calculator spot these 'special case' calculations, which only work when the index x in y^x is a whole number. (When x is not an integer, y^x for negative y is a complex number, of the kind discussed in Chapter 3.) In one of the 1976 numbers of the *Hewlett-Packard Journal*, D. W. Harms describes how the HP-91 calculator algorithms were designed to give these 'special case' powers of negative numbers, and also to give results such as $2^3 = 8$ exactly. The earlier HP-35 calculator algorithms gave $2^3 = 8.000000003$ because of small rounding errors during the process of translating into and out of log language; the HP-91 avoids this by retaining a few more decimal places during the calculation and then quoting the result to the nearest ten significant figures, which replaces the final 3 by 0.

2.3. Multiplication convention

In Chapter 1 we used $\times$ to mean multiply. Here and in later chapters we shall go over to the following common shorthand notation: *If x and y are symbols for numbers then xy means x times y.*

In sections 3.15 and 4.15 we deal with the multiplication of complex numbers and matrices. We use the same convention there: for example, if a and b are matrices then ab denotes a times b. This convention is so familiar that it often traps the unwary, since the *meaning* of 'times' may not be the same in all cases, even though the *notation* is similar. For example, ab and ba mean the same thing if a and b are ordinary numbers, but they do *not* mean the same thing if a and b are matrices. Even for ordinary numbers the multiplication convention only makes unambiguous sense when used with *abstract* symbols (x, y, a, b, etc.). Strictly speaking, 2 and 3 are symbols for 'the number two' and 'the number three' respectively, and yet we usually read 23 as 'twenty-three' rather than 2×3.

In working out a product xy of two numbers using logs (as explained in the preceding section), logs to any base could be used. Ordinary log tables use base 10, but the special number e ($= 2.7182818\ldots$) is often used as the base of logs in scientific work. Log to the base e of x is often denoted $\ln x$ in the scientific literature, the ln standing for 'natural log'. The natural log has the useful property that $\ln(1+x)$ is very closely approximated by x when x is small. In section 3.5 we shall look at the functions $(1+x)^{\frac{1}{2}}$ and $(1+x)^{-1}$; they also are given by simple formulae when x is small. Section 4.6 explains some of the special properties of the number e.

2.4. Error estimation (or the virtue of humility)

Before proceeding to describe a few typical calculations, I must warn readers to keep a sense of proportion when using their calculators. It is easy to get a sense of power from the use of an accurate calculator (just as some people get a sense of power from a high-speed automobile), and we might be tempted to give an impossibly accurate answer to a problem just because our calculator actually shows us eight or more figures. Indeed, it is not unknown for scientists to quote numerical results in the nine- or ten-figure form in which they emerge from a computer, even though the theory which was used to calculate the numbers is only an approximate one!

Let us suppose that we measure the dimensions of a rectangular floor-space using a tape measure. The problem of 'getting the ends right', or of 'joining on', if the floor is longer than the measure, means that we can only get an approximate result. We might claim, for example, that we have got the lengths correct to the nearest centimetre. According to the convention explained in section 1.1, if we say that a length is 3.75 metres (that is, 3 metres and 75 centimetres) we mean that it is nearer to 3.75 than to 3.74 or 3.76. This means, then, that it is between 3.755 and 3.745. If we use the same convention to say that the width is 2.13 metres, then we can use the formula for the area of a rectangle (area = length × width) to work out the following three products:

$$3.755 \times 2.135 = 8.016925$$
$$3.75 \times 2.13 \ \ = 7.9875$$
$$3.745 \times 2.125 = 7.958125.$$

Note how the results illustrate the rule mentioned previously that the number of decimal places in the product (ab) is the sum of the number of places in the numbers a and b. What the numbers show is that we can only say with confidence that the area is between 8.017 and 7.958; we could state this concisely thus:

$$\text{Area} = 7.987 \pm 0.030.$$

This 'x plus or minus y' way of presenting a result is very common in scientific work and often carries with it an implication that the result is *more likely* to be near to x than to be near to $x + y$ or $x - y$. In this simple case we could actually repeat the measurements a few times and check whether the calculated area comes out more often near to x (i.e., 7.987) than near to $x \pm y$. We can see one thing very clearly: the maximum possible error in the area (0.030) is much greater than that in the lengths (0.005). This means that we cannot simply say that the *whole* of a calculation is accurate 'to so many decimal places'; we have to say something about the way in which errors increase throughout the calculation. Here we are dealing with an 'error-amplifying' kind of calculation; later on we shall see that in some special problems one can have 'error-diminishing' calculations (the so-called 'iterative' calculations). The simplest way to get such a calculation is to run an error-amplifying calculation backwards. (In this respect simple mathematical formulae are not like electronic amplifiers or sausage machines; they often work backwards!) To run the present calculation backwards would involve getting two numbers (length and width) from one number (the area). We cannot do this, but we can use the square root key on a calculator to find the length of side of a square with the given area. This length has a mathematical name: it is called the *geometric mean* of the length and width. To be precise, of course, we should define the geometric mean for numbers (not lengths):

Geometric mean of a and $b = \sqrt{(ab)}$.

The reader may check with his calculator that the square roots of the three areas given above can be written in the form 2.826 ± 0.005, showing correctly that there is an error of about 0.005 involved in the length measurements.

To produce a simple formula which gives the error in (ab) from the errors in a and b separately we must use the idea of *percentage error*. If the error in the length is ± 0.005 in 3.75, the percentage error is the name given to the quantity

$$\frac{\pm 0.005}{3.75} \times 100 = \pm 0.13\%.$$

Similarly the percentage error in the width is 0.23%, while that in the area is

$$\frac{\pm 0.030}{7.987} \times 100 = \pm 0.38\%.$$

The reader may make up a few similar examples, and will note that a certain regularity emerges from the results: the sum of the first two numbers is very close to the third one (in our example $0.13 + 0.23 = 0.36$, not far from 0.38). The guiding rule which emerges is the following: *the percentage error in the product* ab *is the sum of the percentage errors in* a *and* b *separately*. This rule is accurate when the percentage errors involved are small (less than about 10%). In accord with our aim of 'making a little go a long way', let us see how this simple rule about multiplication will give us (after a little reasoning) a rule about division. We write down our result, using the short symbol $e(ab)$ for the percentage error in ab, and the symbols $e(a)$ and $e(b)$ for the percentage errors in a and b respectively. We have

$$e(ab) = e(a) + e(b).$$

If these two numbers, on the left and on the right, are equal, we get two more equal numbers by subtracting the same number $e(b)$ from each side. Alternatively, if we get $e(ab)$ by adding $e(a)$ to $e(b)$, we can get back to $e(a)$ by 'undoing' this – that is, by subtracting $e(b)$ from $e(ab)$. We find the result

$$e(a) = e(ab) - e(b).$$

Suppose we give the number ab the new name c; we then know that b is simply $(c \div a)$, and with the new symbols the equation becomes

$$e(c \div b) = e(c) - e(b).$$

It appears, then, that as a logical consequence of our previous rule we must have a further rule: the percentage error in $(c \div b)$ equals the percentage error in c minus the percentage error in b. However, this doesn't make sense, since it appears to mean that if we are uncertain by 5% about *both* b and c we shall be exact in our estimate of $c \div b$! Now, if both b and c were 5% *high*, we *would* get an exact value for $c \div b$, but we don't know this to be so; b may be 5% high and c 5% low, making $c \div b$ wrong by 10%. To look at it another way, when we say that the error is $\pm 5\%$ we are entitled *mathematically* to put $e = 5\%$ or $e = -5\%$ in the equations. Accordingly, if we insist on thinking of $e(c)$ and $e(b)$ as *positive* numbers, to which $\pm$ is prefixed, we must set

$$e(c \div b) = e(c) + e(b),$$

making the results the same for both multiplication and division!

2.5. Simple and compound interest

The most obvious everyday calculations which can use the K constant are those involving value added tax (V.A.T.), interest rates and income tax rates. Some calculators have a percentage key, as was mentioned in section 1, but there is no great difference between the key stroke sequences

$$[\![3.58 \; + \; 8\% \; =]\!] \quad \boxed{3.8664} \quad \text{and}$$
$$[\![3.58 \; \times \; 1.08 \; =]\!] \quad \boxed{3.8664}$$

which both add 8% to £3.58. All we have to remember is that adding 8% to a number is the same as multiplying it by 1.08, and that the result has to be interpreted as £3.87 if we take it to the nearest penny. To be sure of avoiding error we could add $t\%$ tax to an amount s by the following standard key strokes:

$$[\![t \; \div \; 100 \; + \; 1 \; \times \; s \; =]\!]$$

although it doesn't take long to get used to working out the multiplying factor (e.g., 1.08) by mental arithmetic. To work out the products of a series of numbers (a, b, c, etc.) with 1.08 on a calculator with automatic K constant we use the key strokes

$$[\![\times \; 1.08 \; = \; a \; = \; b \; = \; c \; =]\!] \text{ etc.}$$

(The initial strokes, before a, set up the K constant operation as 'multiply by 1.08'.)

To study the way in which a sum of, say, £120 grows at 8% simple interest per year and at 8% compound interest per year we use the automatic K constant facility. The compound interest case can be treated as follows:

⟦120 × 1.08 =⟧ ⬚129.6 ⟦=⟧ ⬚139.968 ⟦=⟧.

On a calculator which has a percentage key as well as an automatic K constant, the sequence

⟦120 + 8 % = = =⟧

will also suffice for the compound interest calculation. The simple interest problem is actually the more awkward, and is perhaps best done by working out the total accrued interest first, using the key strokes below. Note that it is not necessary to use ⟦=⟧ after the 8, since the calculator works out 'the result so far' as soon as the ⟦+⟧ key is pressed.

⟦120 × .08 +⟧ ⬚9.6 ⟦=⟧ ⬚19.2 ⟦=⟧.

(For those few calculators in which the first number in a product is the one stored as the K constant factor, the key stroke sequences will of course need slight modification.)

The results of the calculation are as shown below, illustrating the way in which the compound interest amount gradually outstrips the simple interest amount:

Years	Compound	Simple
0	120	120
2	140	139
4	163	158
6	190	178
8	222	197
10	259	216

The kind of calculation used for the compound interest example is also relevant for other things. For example, the result $(1.11)^7 = 2.076$ shows us that an inflation rate of 11% per year will cause prices to double in roughly seven years (not the nine years suggested by the result, $1 \div 0.11 = 9.09$, which refers to a simple-interest kind of process).

The table of results above was arrived at by using our basic key stroke sequences and reading off the answer every two steps. It would be more efficient, if we particularly wanted to treat two-year intervals, to use the appropriate factor $(1.08)^2$ to replace 1.08 in the compound interest calculation. However, there are very few calculators which can accept a key sequence such as

$$[120 \times 1.08 \ x^2 = + = =]$$

and retain the $[\times \ (1.08)^2]$ as the K constant operation. A notable exception which *can* do this, and indeed could do it for any power of 1.08, is the Sinclair Enterprise, a very small and efficient programmable calculator. It is perhaps unique in that its automatic K constant operation can also be used as part of a program. In the majority of calculators, the sequence given above would first produce $120 \times 1.08 = 129.6$ and then square it.

On a calculator with memory we could use the sequence

$$[1.08 \times = MS] \quad \text{or} \quad [1.08 \ x^2 \ MS]$$

followed by

$$[120 \times MR = =]$$

to accomplish the desired end of working in two-year intervals. The CBM 899D, which has brackets, can do this calculation with the sequence

$$[120 \times (1.08 \times =) = = =]$$

and the power of 1.08 involved can be adjusted by means of the number of $[=]$ strokes inside the brackets.

2.6. Mortgages

Suppose that a home-buyer borrows £5000 from a building society, at an interest rate of 11% per year. After a year he pays back an amount p (for payment). However, he is then supposed to owe £5000 × 1.11 after interest has been charged for a year, so he still owes them the amount

$$a_1 = (5000 \times 1.11) - p.$$

This amount a_1 is now regarded as the starting size of the loan; after a further year the borrower pays the fixed amount p again, and now owes an amount

$$a_2 = (a_1 \times 1.11) - p.$$

After three years he owes

$$a_3 = (a_2 \times 1.11) - p,$$

and so on. If we took a simple-minded approach we might reason as follows. To pay back £5000 in twenty years requires £250 per year, but that corresponds to having zero interest rate. On the other hand if the payment is £5000 × 0.11 = £550 per year, that would leave the borrower owing £5000 permanently! The annual repayment needed to pay the debt in twenty years thus rises from £250 to some amount p (greater than £550) as the interest rate rises from 0% to 11%. On a calculator with memory the key strokes

$$[\![p \ \text{MS} \ 5000 \ \times \ 1.11 \ - \ \text{MR} \ \times \ 1.11 \ - \ \text{MR} \ \times \ 1.11 \ - \ \text{MR}]\!] \ldots$$

will display the successive values a_1, a_2, etc. After a certain number of years the amount owed will fall to zero, that is, the mortgage will be paid off. The formula which gives the rate p so that $a_n = 0$ (i.e., so that n years are needed to pay off the mortgage) can be worked out by using the mathematics of geometric series, and is most easily remembered as follows:

$$p = \text{interest due for first year} \times \frac{r^n}{(r^n - 1)},$$

where r is the compound interest multiplying factor $1 + i$ (as a decimal). For our example the sum s is £5000, the interest rate i (as a decimal) is 0.11 and the multiplying factor $r = 1 + i$ is 1.11. The value of p to give a full repayment after twenty years is obtained by setting $n = 20$ in the formula. We find:

$$p = £5000 \times 0.11 \times (1.11)^{20} \div (1.11^{20} - 1),$$

which gives $p = £627.88$. We can now work out the 'amounts owed', a_1, a_2, etc., and obtain the following table:

Years	Debt	Annual Loan Repayment
0	5000	
1	4922	78
2	4836	86
3	4740	96
...	...	...

Years	Debt	Annual Loan Repayment
18	1075	459
19	566	509
20	0	566

The total amount paid by the end of the twenty years is £12,558 on an original loan of £5000. In the first year the interest is £5000 × 0.11 = £550, so that the payment of £627.88 pays this off and leaves £77.88 (as we show) to reduce the original debt. This is what is meant by the conventional statement that in the early years most of each mortgage payment goes to pay interest on the loan. To convert the £627.88 annual repayment into *monthly* repayments we divide by twelve: £627.88 ÷ 12 = £52.32. In fact if the borrower pays this amount monthly he is actually paying slightly more than 11% per year on his loan, since, for example, he has not borrowed £5000 for *all* of the first year. It seems to be the practice for building societies to mean the lower figure (11% in our case) when they quote their lending rate; the true rate is around a quarter of a per cent higher.

If the rate changes while the mortgage is being repaid (as it is certain to do!), we can work through the calculation of the debt year by year, putting in a new value for *r* at the appropriate year. The change will occur part way through some year, so we need to use a 'weighted average' for that particular year – e.g., 10% for three months followed by 11% for nine months is equivalent to 10.75% for the year, since

$$\tfrac{1}{12}[(3 \times 10) + (9 \times 11)] = 10.75.$$

Having got the amount of debt at the end of that year, we can think of it as a new loan *s* taken out at the new rate of 11%, and apply the formula for *p* to find the payments needed in order to pay off the debt in a further *n* years.

To use the formula for *p* we must work out numbers such as $(1.11)^{20} \div [(1.11)^{20} - 1]$. The routine way to work out $(1.11)^{20}$ on a machine with automatic K constant is to use the key strokes

$[\![1.11 \quad \times \quad = \ldots]\!]$ (19 $[\![=]\!]$ strokes) $\boxed{8.0623095}$.

Another way is to use the law of indices, which tells us that $(1.11)^{20} = [(1.11)^5]^4$; the key strokes for this approach are

$[1.11 \times = = = = \times = \times =]$ $\boxed{8.0623104}$.

The second sequence is much shorter and more accurate, since the rounding errors increase with the number of operations performed. The results shown were obtained on a CBM 899D calculator; the accurate answer is $(1.11)^{20} = 8.0623115$. For the mortgage calculation the errors are not important enough to cause a problem. To work out the complete fraction $(1.11)^{20} \div [(1.11)^{20} - 1]$ it is easy to subtract the 1 mentally and do the correct division. Alternatively, with $(1.11)^{20}$ in the display, the strokes

$[\div = = - 1 \div = = \pm]$ $\boxed{1.1415966}$

work out the fraction at one go. If readers first divide every term of the required fraction by $(1.11)^{20}$, they should by now be able to see how this sequence works.

2.7. Building society investments

The money which the building society uses to make the loans comes from the investors, and they receive interest on *their* loans. The society, of course, pays out less interest than it receives from borrowers, to pay for running costs and various other outlays on officers and offices (whose prolific breeding has been commented on in the newspapers from time to time!). Suppose that a building society offers an investment which pays 8% per year net, equivalent to 11.94% gross at the standard rate of tax. This implies that for every £100 invested it *would* pay £11.94 to the investor, but it actually pays £8.00, because it has to subtract tax before making the payment. The ratio $8 \div 11.94$ is equal to 0.670, which is the same as $1 - 0.330$. This shows that 33% of the £11.94 has been deducted as tax. It seems likely that the society doesn't actually start such a scheme by thinking at the '11.94 end', but rather at the '8 end', with the 11.94 thrown in as the 'effective' interest rate, which is singularly *in*effective, since the investor cannot reclaim the tax paid on his behalf. For example, if the basic tax rate changes, the payment still stays at 8%, rather than moving up or down as it would if there were a basic true rate of 11.94%.

We can investigate an example in a little more detail. The leaflets of a building society advertise two-year investment certificates. The interest rate is 8.5% per year, and the investor who puts in £1000 can either have a matured sum of £1181 after two years or take an annual income of £85 (paid in two instalments per year). This example lends itself nicely to an analysis in terms of the ideas of simple and compound interest which we have already studied. The rate of 8.5% per year is being interpreted to mean $\frac{1}{2} \times 8.5\% = 4.25\%$ every six months, so that £1000 after six months yields £42.50. If this is now taken by the investor, it leaves £1000, and the process repeats every six months. This amounts to doing a simple interest calculation using an annual interest rate of 8.5%. After two years the interest yielded is $2 \times £85 = £170$ for an initial £1000 investment. If the investor lets the total amount stay invested, then after one year (i.e., two six-month periods) we have to use the compound interest multiplying factor $(1.0425)^2 = 1.0868$. This shows that the annual rate is really 8.68%, a little higher than the nominal rate of 8.5%, if the sum is allowed to grow at compound interest. After two years the £1000 grows to $£1000 \times (1.0425)^4 = £1181$, while a £1170 total results from the other alternative.

2.8. Hire purchase

The difference between true and apparent interest rates is perhaps most marked in the field of hire purchase arrangements, so much so that legislation has been passed to ensure that the prospective buyer receives clear information about the true interest he will have to pay. Suppose a customer buys something for £300, and has to pay 20% of that at once (the minimum percentage which this deposit can be is nowadays often subject to government control). He pays £60, and so still owes £240. The finance company operating the hire purchase system pays the residual amount to the store and then recovers the £240 from the customer at, say, 10% interest per year for two years. (The maximum time of payment is also often subject to government control.) What this 10% *means*, however, is that the *total* percentage $(2 \times 10\% = 20\%)$ interest is charged on the £240, making the total amount repaid equal to $£240 \times 1.2 = £288$. This is then split up into twenty-four equal monthly payments of £12. The total cost of the goods is thus $£288 + £60 = £348$, and they are technically on loan to the buyer, only becoming his property when the payments are completed. If we compare this calculation with the one which deals with mortgage repayments, we see that the mortgage arrangement is fairer, since it partly makes allowance for the fact that the original sum is not being borrowed for the whole of the repayment time. Thus, a sum of £240, repaid in twenty-four months at a mortgage interest rate of 10% per year, would involve payments of £11.52 per month, as we find by using the formula given earlier for calculating mortgage repayments.

2.9. Areas and volumes

If we think of the area of a rectangle quite literally as the number of unit squares which it contains, it is clear that the area is given by the product of the lengths of the sides. For example $3 \times 2 = 6$:

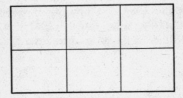

and we get 6 square centimetres if we have sides of length 2 cm and 3 cm. Of course, we use this product rule even when the lengths of the sides are not whole numbers, and end up with areas which involve fractions of a square centimetre, or square inch, or whatever unit we use. From the picture above we can visualize an important principle: if we measure in, say, half centimetres as units, we get *four* times as many little squares, not twice as many, since both sides contain twice as many length units. Thus, the change from the centimetre unit to the half centimetre unit means that area numbers multiply by four and length numbers multiply by two. The basic principle is that the number which gives the area multiplies by k^2 if the numbers giving the lengths multiply by k. We have tried to state this carefully, since it is not the *physical area* which changes but the *number* which represents it. If we change from inches to centimetres, for example, the length numbers multiply by

2.54, since a centimetre is shorter than an inch. The area numbers multiply by $(2.54)^2 = 6.45$, and this is true for areas enclosed by planar boundaries of any kind, whether rectangles, triangles, circles or squiggly closed curves. On the other hand, if we actually expanded the shape itself (e.g., by making the sides of the rectangle in the picture twice as long), the area will increase by a factor k^2 if the lengths increase by a factor k. Thus, binoculars with a *linear* magnification of 8 give an *area* magnification of $8^2 = 64$, which sounds more impressive when used by an unscrupulous advertiser. A symbol such as 8×30 stamped on binoculars usually means that 8 is the linear magnification, while the 30 indicates that the diameter of the objective lens is 30 millimetres.

From the preceding kind of reasoning it follows that the area of a circle should be proportional to the square of its radius r or its diameter d. The constant of proportionality involves the number π, equal to $3.14159265\ldots$, and scientific calculators usually have a special π key, which puts this number into the display when it is pressed. The rough approximation $\frac{22}{7}$ ($= 3.1428\ldots$) is sometimes used as being an easily remembered number, or alternatively the approximation $\pi^2 = 10$ is easy to remember (actually $\pi^2 = 9.869\ldots$). The formulae giving the area and perimeter of a circle are

Area $= \pi r^2 = \frac{1}{4}\pi d^2$
Perimeter $= 2\pi r = \pi d$.

(The perimeter of any fixed shape will multiply by a factor k if the dimensions in all directions are multiplied by factor k.) It is clear that a circle of diameter 1 can be drawn within a unit square:

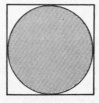

The circle visibly has smaller area than the square, which fits with the numerical result that $\pi/4 = 0.785\ldots$ is less than 1. The

circle's area is thus roughly three quarters of that of the square.

The area of shapes such as triangles and parallelograms can be

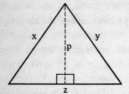 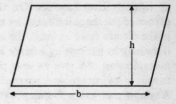

worked out using formulae which involve angles and functions such as $\sin \theta$, but it is also possible to use formulae which involve only lengths, and which therefore can be used with a simple non-scientific calculator. (Sines and cosines are treated later in the book.) The formulae for the areas of a parallelogram and triangle are as follows (using the lengths shown in the diagrams):

Parallelogram: hb

Triangle: $\sqrt{s(s-x)(s-y)(s-z)}$

or $\frac{1}{2}(zp)$.

In the above formulae h is the vertical height of the parallelogram, *not* the length of the slanting sides; s is the semi-perimeter of the triangle, i.e., half of the perimeter, or $\frac{1}{2}(x+y+z)$; p is the vertical height of the triangle.

In the case of *volumes* our general discussion about the effect of using length multiplying factor k can be used again if we use a volume multiplying factor k^3; e.g., 1 cubic inch is $(2.54)^3 = 16.39$ cubic centimetres (cc). The volume and surface area of a sphere are

Volume $= \frac{4}{3}\pi r^3 = \frac{1}{6}\pi d^3$

Area $= 4\pi r^2 = \pi d^2$.

In general if an object, such as a box or a cylinder, can be imagined as sliced into *identical* horizontal parallel layers of such a shape that the (identical) area of each one can be calculated, then the volume of the object is equal to the area of each strip multiplied by the vertical height of the object. For an object such as a cone this slicing into identical layers cannot be done, but it is easy to remember that the volume of a circular cone is $\frac{1}{3}$ of the volume $\pi r^2 h$ of a cylinder with the same vertical height h and base radius r.

Historically, the metre was defined to be one forty-millionth part of the earth's circumference (as then known). If we regard the earth as a sphere of radius r and its equatorial circumference as a circle of radius r, we can thus set (for the circumference c):

$$c = 2\pi r = 40,000 \text{ kilometres.}$$

However, we also have for the earth's volume v the formula

$$v = \frac{4}{3}\pi r^3.$$

We can *either* work out r and then find v, i.e., make two numerical calculations, *or* we can do some algebra to get a single formula which gives v in terms of c:

$$v = \frac{c^3}{6\pi^2} = \frac{(40,000)^3}{60}$$
$$= \frac{4^3 \times (10^4)^3}{6 \times 10} = \frac{64 \times 10^{12}}{(6 \times 10)},$$

i.e., about 10^{12} cubic kilometres. In the calculation we have used the simplifying approximation that π^2 (about 9.87) can be replaced by 10, and have also separated out the powers of 10 (as explained in Chapter 1), since we would produce overflow if we attempted to cube 40,000 on a simple calculator.

2.10. Average speed: a use for reciprocals

Suppose that a driver is in a hurry to get somewhere, and he knows that the first half of his route is through a built-up area, while the second half, although of equal distance, is along a motorway. Being a law-abiding mathematician, he traverses the built-up area at 30 miles per hour; what speed should he maintain along the motorway to obtain an average speed of 40 m.p.h. for the whole journey? Many people answering this question quickly tend to say '50 m.p.h.', because 40 is the average of 30 and 50. However, the correct answer is 60 m.p.h.; to see this we have to divert our attention from the speeds, to which it is directed by the wording of the problem, and think about the *times* involved in the two halves of the journey. (This search for the crucial variable to study is often an important part of problem-solving, even in advanced scientific work.) The driver wants to arrive on time; if he travels l miles at 30 m.p.h. this takes a time

$$t_1 = \frac{\text{Distance}}{\text{Speed}} = \frac{l}{30}.$$

Going the next l miles at speed v_2 takes the time

$$t_2 = \frac{l}{v_2}.$$

To go the whole $2l$ miles at a speed of 40 m.p.h. would take the time

$$t = \frac{2l}{40}.$$

To arrive exactly on time we must arrange things so that

$$\frac{l}{30} + \frac{l}{v_2} = \frac{2l}{40} = \frac{l}{20}.$$

Since l appears in every term in this equation the solution v_2 will not depend on l, so it won't make any difference if we replace l by the number 1 in the equation. The equation involves reciprocals; on a calculator with a reciprocal key we get the reciprocal of 20 (i.e., $\frac{1}{20}$) by the key strokes 20 $\frac{1}{x}$. On a calculator with automatic K constant the K constant sequence $[\![20 \div = =]\!]$ works; it gives the displays 20, 1, 0.05 in turn. If we have none of the above facilities we must use the sequence $[\![1 \div 20 =]\!]$ to work out $\frac{1}{20}$. Working out $\frac{1}{30}$ gives 0.0333..., with the 3s repeating, since $\frac{1}{30}$ has a decimal number form which 'goes on forever', whereas $\frac{1}{20}$ has a decimal form which stops at the 5 in 0.05 (we should strictly say that an infinite string of 0s follows the 5, but, of course, we ignore this in calculations). By trying a few guesses for v_2 the reader should find that $v_2 = 50$ doesn't fit, whereas $v_2 = 60$ does; the numbers are

$$\frac{1}{30} + \frac{1}{50} = 0.05333...$$
$$\frac{1}{30} + \frac{1}{60} = 0.04999...$$
$$\frac{1}{20} = 0.05.$$

Here we see a practical point which must be remembered when a calculator is used: the calculator only works to so many (e.g., eight) figures, so that we have to learn to spot when it is 'trying to tell us something'. In this case, the $0.04999\ldots$, with a string of nines, is the best the calculator can do to indicate 0.05, because we started it off with a number ($\frac{1}{30}$) which it couldn't get exactly right, as we pointed out earlier. With a little thought we can usually sort out these special cases and correct the displayed result, although such time for clear thought is not always available under examination conditions – it was recently commented by a marker of A-level examination papers that many candidates using calculators had given the answer 1.4999 to a problem instead of spotting that the answer should have been 1.5. The way to proceed when in doubt about the solution to any equation is to stick the proposed solution into the equation and see if it works (i.e., use the 'suck it and see' method, which is perhaps better denoted by S.I.A.S. to maintain some mathematical decorum). For our particular example we can check easily; since $\frac{1}{30}$ is actually $2 \times \frac{1}{60}$ and $\frac{1}{20}$ is $3 \times \frac{1}{60}$, we see that our solution ($v_2 = 60$) is exact. In units of $\frac{1}{60}$ the equation becomes $2 + 1 = 3$, which is correct. This idea of using the correct units helps us to find the correct general formula for v_2, so that a trial and error method is not needed. We argue as follows: the unknown speed v_2 must obey the equation

$$\frac{1}{v_2} = \frac{2}{40} - \frac{1}{30},$$

from which we see directly that $v_2 = 60$. Suppose now that v and v_1 are arbitrary numbers; we have

$$\frac{1}{v_2} = \frac{2}{v} - \frac{1}{v_1}.$$

To use units of size $\frac{1}{v} \times \frac{1}{v_1}$ we multiply the equation by vv_1, to get

$$\frac{vv_1}{v_2} = 2v_1 - v.$$

This shows that vv_1 is the product of v_2 and $2v_1 - v$, so that

$$v_2 = vv_1 \div (2v_1 - v).$$

In key stroke notation $[\![2 \times v_1 - v \div v_1 \div v_2 =]\!]$ works out $1/v_2$, and then we take a reciprocal to get v_2. Readers who are experienced at dealing with algebraic equations may wonder why we bothered with the idea of 'scale-change algebra'. It is, of course, because we are trying to gain some insight into the algebra. Readers who know a little *more* mathematics will note that the idea of 'scale-invariance' of an equation, although used in theoretical physics, does not seem to have been tried so much in the teaching of elementary mathematics.

Having obtained a definite formula we can do the calculation for various values of the speeds. Let us, rather, complete our discussion with a simple calculation using our original numbers. If the driver sticks to a speed of 50 m.p.h. over the second half of his journey, and if we take the length of the whole journey (i.e., $2l$) to be 40 miles, then he takes the total time

$$\tfrac{20}{30} + \tfrac{20}{50} = 1.0666\ldots \text{ hrs}$$

for the journey. By going at 60 m.p.h. over the second half he would have achieved an average speed of 40 m.p.h., as we have already calculated, so he would have taken a time of 1 hour for the total journey. The time difference is $0.066\ldots$ hr, which is 4 minutes, not really much in an hour's journey. There is a moral here for car drivers!

2.11. The 'there and back' problem

Aeroplanes crossing the Atlantic sometimes are helped along by a following wind, or jet stream, which shortens the journey time. This fact suggests the following problem: if an aeroplane flies from A to B and back, and the wind (of speed w) makes the aeroplane's speed $v + w$ one way and $v - w$ the other way, does the wind effect alter the aeroplane's average speed for the round trip for better or for worse? If l is the distance from A to B, the total journey is of length $2l$, so we have a problem like that discussed in the preceding section. The total time for the round trip is

$$t = \frac{l}{v+w} + \frac{l}{v-w}.$$

Suppose that we fix l at, say, 4000. Setting $v = 500$ and $w = 10$, 20, 30, etc. into the calculator, we see that t increases with w. This suggests that we try to *prove* this in a way which does not involve using particular v and w values. Using units of size $(v+w)^{-1} \times (v-w)^{-1}$ the equation for t becomes

$$t(v+w)(v-w) = l(v-w) + l(v+w).$$

We can use the distributive law $xy + xz = x(y+z)$ to simplify the right-hand side:

$$\begin{aligned} l(v-w) + l(v+w) &= l(v-w+v+w) \\ &= 2lv \end{aligned}$$

and also can simplify the left-hand side as follows:

$$\begin{aligned} (v+w)(v-w) &= v^2 + wv - vw - w^2 \\ &= v^2 - w^2. \end{aligned}$$

The final result is

$$t = \frac{2lv}{(v^2 - w^2)}.$$

Now since the square w^2 is some positive number, it follows that increasing w makes $v^2 - w^2$ smaller. Since we *divide* by this quantity, it follows that t is *increased* as w increases from zero. Thus we cannot get any wind speed which improves the round trip time. Since the wind speed varies with altitude, an aeroplane doesn't have to operate with exactly the same w value on both parts of its journey, and our calculation is perhaps better suited to the situation of a boat moving in a river which has a current of speed w. Even then w may vary because of tidal effects. In fact, the calculation which we have done was actually used in the Michelson–Morley experiment – a famous event in the history of the theory of relativity. The basic idea of it is that, if there is some universal fluid (the aether) in which light waves travel, a light beam travelling on a round trip (e.g., to a mirror and back) will have different ingoing and outgoing speeds if there is an aether current of speed w. We have just seen that any non-zero w increases the round trip time, and the Michelson–Morley experiment measured this effect by a clever method involving the use of interference fringes caused by the light waves. That the results always led to the conclusion $w = 0$ was taken to indicate that the light moves with the same speed on both halves of its journey, so that the notion of an underlying aether fluid does not seem to be necessary.

The 'there and back' problem provides us with an interesting example of mathematical reasoning, which can be explained by means of an example. Suppose that a man goes 15 miles up river and then back (a total of 30 miles) in a motorboat which goes at 10 m.p.h. in still water. The journey time will differ slightly from 3 hours if the river has a steady current of speed w. Call the journey time $t(w)$. One of the basic tricks of mathematics is the use of power series (series involving powers of some quantity), and we might guess that there is some formula for $t(w)$ like the following:

$$t(w) = 3 + aw + bw^2 + \text{higher power terms,}$$

where a and b are unknown numbers. For $w = 0$ we get $t = 3$, which is correct, since for zero current the round trip takes 3 hours. Now, we can also say that a *is zero*. Why? Well, if we reverse the current, from, say 1 m.p.h. to -1 m.p.h., the *round trip* still takes exactly the same time (think about it!). Our formula cannot give this result (i.e., $3 + a = 3 - a$) unless a is zero. To find b we take a small w value, $w = 1$, say, and work out the round trip time,

$$t = \tfrac{15}{11} + \tfrac{15}{9} = 3.0303 \text{ hrs.}$$

This shows that we should take b to be 0.0303 (i.e., $\tfrac{1}{33}$ as a fraction) and we can check, for example, for $w = 2$ that

$$t = \tfrac{15}{12} + \tfrac{15}{8} = 3.125 \text{ hrs,}$$

whereas the formula would give

$$t = 3 + \tfrac{1}{33} \times (2^2) = 3.121 \text{ hrs,}$$

which is fairly close. For larger w values, of course, the higher powers of w in the formula cannot be ignored (although the w^3 term *can* be ignored. Why?).

2.12. Metres and megahertz

The experimental discovery of radio waves is usually attributed to Hertz, and followed the earlier theoretical work of Maxwell. It is now known that light waves, radio waves, X-rays, gamma rays, etc., are all types of electromagnetic wave. The thing which distinguishes the different types from one another is their wavelength. For example, visible light waves have wavelengths of around 6000 Ångström units; this unit is 10^{-8} cm, so that 6000 of them represent 6×10^{-5} cm (less than one ten-thousandth of a centimetre). Radio waves, on the other hand, may be as long as thousands of metres; for example, the British Light Programme (now Radio 4) uses a wavelength of 1500 metres. 1500 metres is also described as 200 kHz in the *Radio Times*. kHz stands for 'kilohertz' ('kilo' means 'thousands'). The Hertz is the name now used for a frequency of one cycle per second. Thus 200 kHz is 200,000 cycles per second, and this is the frequency of the oscillating electric field in the waves. Strictly speaking, it is only an average frequency: each transmitter produces a small spread of frequencies, and this may overlap with the spread from another transmitter at a neighbouring nominal frequency. On an A.M. (amplitude modulated) transmitter, the higher frequencies in the transmitted sound are on the outside edges of this band. A radio a little off-tune gives a distorted screechy sound because it is picking up only the higher frequencies down one edge of the band. Sometimes, by tuning 'dead centre' and using the tone control to cut out the high frequencies, it is possible to diminish interference from other transmitters. (The directional properties of the aerial in portable radios mean that turning the radio round slowly will also give the position of least interference.) The basic formula which relates the speed, the frequency and the wavelength for any kind of wave motion is

Speed = frequency × wavelength.

If we try this for some numbers taken from the *Radio Times* we get:

Radio 4: $200,000 \times 1500 = 300$ millions
Radio 3: $1,215,000 \times 247 = 300$ millions
Radio 1: $1,053,000 \times 285 = 300$ millions.

We can't work out the above products directly on a simple calculator without remembering to separate out the tens, e.g.

$$1.053 \times 10^6 \times 2.85 \times 10^2 = 3.001 \times 10^8$$

with only the product 1.053×2.85 being worked out on the calculator. *Some* calculators will show E30010500 if we put the big numbers in directly, telling us that something (in this case a 0) has been chopped off the end of the answer. Now, the results above show that the speed of radio waves is 300 million metres per second. If A.F.N. Frankfurt broadcasts on 343 metres, where will it be on a kHz scale? We have only to divide speed by wavelength to get frequency:

$$(300 \times 10^6) \div 343 = 875 \text{ kHz (i.e., } 875 \times 10^3 \text{ Hz).}$$

V.H.F. transmitter frequencies are given in MHz (megahertz; mega means million), so a frequency of 90 MHz corresponds to a wavelength of

$$(300 \times 10^6) \div (90 \times 10^6) = 3.3 \text{ metres.}$$

How long does a radio signal take to travel from earth to astronauts approaching the moon? 300 million metres is 300,000 kilometres. A kilometre is about $\frac{5}{8}$ of a mile, so we estimate the speed of the waves to be 187,000 miles per second (actually 186,000 is the more accurate value). To travel 238,000 miles to the moon would require a time of about $\frac{238}{187} = 1.3$ secs. Such times can be measured accurately nowadays for radar pulses sent to the moon and back, so that the distance to the moon becomes the thing which can be calculated. It is often said that 'light from the sun takes eight minutes to reach us'. To cover a distance of 92 million miles at 186,000 miles per second takes 495 seconds, so the statement is a reasonable approximation, particularly since the earth–sun distance varies a little throughout the year.

When light travels through transparent matter such as water or glass, the different wavelengths in it (corresponding to different colours) have slightly different speeds. This means that a glass prism bends the different colours in white light differently, so splitting up the light to give the spectrum; water droplets in the air act similarly, giving the rainbow. The glass lenses in a telescope also give this colour splitting (when we do not want it) and give coloured edges to objects being viewed unless specially designed achromatic ('not coloured') lenses are used.

In free space light of all wavelengths travels at the same speed c.

If light of wavelength λ travels at speed $v(\lambda)$ in some materials, the ratio $\mu(\lambda) = c \div v(\lambda)$ is called the *refractive index* of the material for light of that wavelength. (The refractive index also appears in section 4.5 of this book.) The refractive index of water for red light is 1.329 and that for violet light is 1.343; these colours are at opposite sides of the rainbow (according to Roy G. Biv). The speed of violet light in water is thus

$$v = \frac{c}{1.343} = \frac{3 \times 10^8}{1.343}$$
$$= 2.234 \times 10^8 \text{ metres per second.}$$

One of the popular sayings arising from relativity theory is that 'matter cannot travel faster than light'. However, some elementary particles *can* travel faster than $\frac{c}{1.343}$ (although slower than c) in water, and when they do so they set up 'light shock waves' which are seen as a bluish glow called Cerenkov radiation.

2.13. Cube roots from square roots

The square root key has been used to advantage in several of the calculations which we have discussed in this chapter (e.g., sections 2.2, 2.3). Most inexpensive calculators nowadays have such a key, but very few have a cube root key. The Canon Canola desk calculator has one, but is not a calculator of the simple type which we are discussing. Many scientific calculators have a powering key, marked x^y or y^x, which will find arbitrary powers, e.g., $(1.327)^{2.51}$; to find $(1.327)^{\frac{1}{3}}$ involves the key strokes

$[\![1.327 \ y^x \ 3 \ 1/x \ =]\!]$ $\boxed{1.098897}$

on a calculator such as the T.I.58 or the Sinclair Enterprise calculator, which work out the above expression as

$$1.327 \ y^x(3\tfrac{1}{x}) = (1.327)^{\frac{1}{3}}$$

rather than as

$$(1.327 \ y^x \ 3)\tfrac{1}{x} = (1.327)^{-3}.$$

Some calculators (e.g., the CBM SR 4148R) not only work according to the first key sequence above, but also have an explicit

$\sqrt[3]{}\,y$ key which will give the cube root by means of the sequence

$[\![1.327 \;\; \sqrt[3]{}\,y]\!]$ $\boxed{0.28292076}$ $[\![3 \;=]\!]$ $\boxed{1.098897}$.

The intermediate display, which at first might lead the operator to suspect an error, is the log (to base e) of 1.327, since the calculator is using the 'log translation' procedure outlined in section 2.2. Strictly speaking the $\sqrt[3]{}\,y$ key is redundant if the calculator has a y^x key and a reciprocal key, and if the operator can handle the law of indices!

On a simple calculator with a square root key we can get at the cube root of a number by exploiting the law of indices as follows. We note that

$$\tfrac{1}{3} = \tfrac{1}{4} \times \tfrac{4}{3} = \tfrac{1}{4} \times (1 + \tfrac{1}{3})$$

so that

$$(1.327)^{\frac{1}{3}} = (1.327 \times 1.327^{\frac{1}{3}})^{\frac{1}{4}}.$$

We can get the fourth root of the product in the brackets by using the $\sqrt{}$ key twice, but we still apparently need to know $1.327^{\frac{1}{3}}$ in order to calculate $1.327^{\frac{1}{3}}$. This is *not* so! To illustrate this let us guess that the required cube root is 1.1. If we put this estimate into the bracket on the right we find

$$(1.327 \times 1.1)^{\frac{1}{4}} = 1.099172.$$

Putting *this* number into the bracket and repeating gives a sequence of numbers, 1.098965, 1.098913, 1.098900, 1.098897, 1.098896, the last number repeating itself if we continue the process. Cubing the last number gives 1.3269964; cubing 1.098897 gives 1.3270001. This illustrates that (apart from a rounding error which might affect the last digit) the repetitive process (usually called an iterative process) does correctly converge (i.e. 'home in') to the correct cube root. To get a good first guess we can note that $\tfrac{1}{3} = 0.333\ldots$ is not very far from $\tfrac{3}{8} = 0.375$, so that the sequence

$[\![1.327 \;\; \times \;\; = \;\; = \;\; \sqrt{} \;\; \sqrt{} \;\; \sqrt{}\,]\!]$ $\boxed{1.111927}$

can be used to avoid guessing ($\tfrac{5}{16}$ gives an even better estimate than $\tfrac{3}{8}$). If the calculator has a memory, the sequence of strokes involved (starting from our guess of 1.1) is

$[\![1.327 \;\; \text{MS} \;\; 1.1 \;\; \times \;\; \text{MR} \;\; = \;\; \sqrt{} \;\; \sqrt{} \;\; \times \;\; \text{MR} \;\; = \;\; \sqrt{} \;\; \sqrt{}\,]\!]$ etc.

To check the behaviour of the iterative process in more detail we work out $8^{\frac{1}{3}}$, which should be exactly 2, using the first guess 2.2. We find the sequence 2.2, 2.048227, 2.011949, 2.00298, 2.000744, 2.000185, 2.000045, 2.00001, 2.000002, 2 exactly. The ratio of the error at each stage to that at the next stage can be checked by the reader to be very close to 4 (which is the theoretical ratio obtained if the process is analysed by means of the differential calculus, which we discuss in section 3.16). The method outlined here thus divides the error by 4 on each cycle of the process, and is a 'slow but sure' means of extracting cube roots. In this book we describe many uses for the square root key, and the interested reader will find further uses for it in an article by W. Wynne Willson in the November 1976 edition of *Mathematics in School*.

Exercises

1. Use the law $(a+b)(c+d) = ac+ad+bc+bd$ to obtain the following rule, which we have used several times in this book: if n(a) denotes the number of decimal places in a number a, then

$$n(ab) = n(a)+n(b).$$

Does the result $1.6 \times 0.35 = 0.56$ obey this equation?

Solution

We can proceed most easily by using an example to show how the reasoning works:

$$1.6 \times 0.36 = (1 + 6 \times 10^{-1}) \times (3 \times 10^{-1} + 6 \times 10^{-2}).$$

The distributive law says that we can work this out by adding four products:

$$3 \times 10^{-1} + 6 \times 10^{-2} + 18 \times 10^{-2} + 36 \times 10^{-3}$$

which can be written as

$$10^{-1} \times (3) + 10^{-2} \times (6+18+3) + 10^{-3} \times 6$$
$$= 10^{-1} \times (3+2) + 10^{-2} \times 7 + 10^{-3} \times 6 = 0.576.$$

It is clear that the 'smallest bit' at the end must be a 10^{-3} type term, that is, a term of type $10^{-(1+2)}$. However, we also find $1.6 \times 0.35 = 0.56$ (i.e., 0.560). Thus we must remember that the last one or more digits *could be zero*; alternatively, we could change the formula for $n(ab)$ by using a $\leqslant$ (less than or equal to) sign instead of $=$. If we change the formula in this way, we can re-write it to apply to division:

$n(a \div b) \geqslant n(a) - n(b)$

e.g., $2.1 \div 6.2 = 0.33870968$ (to eight places).

On multiplying the eight-place number by 6.2 we get a nine-place number, which gives 2.1 *after* it is rounded to seven decimal places (i.e., six zeros follow the 1).

2. In the average speed problem of section 2.10 we found that to get an average speed of v, with a first half speed of v_1, we need a second half speed v_2 given by

$$v_2 = \frac{vv_1}{(2v_1 - v)}.$$

What happens if we only manage to go at speed $\frac{1}{2}v$ for the first half of the journey?

Solution

The formula gives a required v_2 value of $\frac{1}{2}v^2 \div 0$ (i.e., infinite speed) if we set $v_1 = \frac{1}{2}v$. This is because we must cover the second half of the journey in zero time to bring up the average speed for the whole journey to the value v. It is not possible to make the average speed greater than $2v_1$, since the allotted time will all have been used up during the first half of the journey. The formula gives a negative v_2 value if we use a v greater than $2v_1$; this corresponds to having time run backwards on the second half of the journey – not a practical proposition!

3. If a home-buyer has seven years to go to pay off his mortgage, and the interest rate rises from 10% to 11%, by what factor should his repayments be multiplied to keep the repayment time to seven years? How much longer will be needed to pay off the mortgage if the payments are *not* increased?

Solution

The amount s still owed need not be known. We know from the basic formula for the annual repayment rate r that

$r(10\%) = s \times 0.10 \times (1.1)^7 \div [(1.1)^7 - 1]$
      $= 0.2054s$
$r(11\%) = s \times 0.11 \times (1.11)^7 \div [(1.11)^7 - 1]$
      $= 0.2122s$

so that $r(11\%) = r(10\%) \times 1.0332$.

If we keep r the same, but pay for n years, we require that

$$0.2054s = s \times 0.11 \times (1.11)^n \div [(1.11)^n - 1].$$

On a simple calculator with square root key we can work out $\frac{1}{2}$, $\frac{1}{4}$ and $\frac{1}{8}$ powers, and we find by trial and error that the right-hand side equals $0.2049s$ at $n = 7\frac{3}{8}$, so that $\frac{3}{8}$ of a year (i.e., 4 or 5 months) is added to the repayment time.

4. Radar transmitters use microwaves, that is, electromagnetic waves with a wavelength of a few centimetres. What frequency corresponds to a wavelength of 5 cm?

Solution

300 million metres per second is $300 \times 10^6 \times 10^2$ cm per second, since 1 metre $= 100$ centimetres. Writing this as 30×10^9, to make the division easier, we find (see section 2.12)

Frequency $= \dfrac{30 \times 10^9}{5} = 6 \times 10^9$ Hz $= 6 \times 10^3$ mega Hz.

5. If we are uncertain by $\pm 10\%$ about some number x, how uncertain are we about x^2 and $\sqrt{x}$?

Solution

x^2 is really $x \times x$, so that the result of section 2.4 shows that the error in x^2 should be $\pm 20\%$. Actually, if x became $1.1x$, we would increase x^2 by a factor $(1.1)^2 = 1.21$, which means a 21% increase; however, the simple rule of section 2.4 is fairly accurate. If squaring doubles the error, we can see that taking the square root *halves* the error. Thus, if we work out $\sqrt{(1.1x)}$, we get $\sqrt{x} \times 1.049$, which is an increase of 4.9%, or very closely half of the error (10%) in x.

Chapter 3
Simple Mathematics and Science Using Calculators

3.1. Some useful results

Before proceeding further, we pause for a moment to take stock of some of the practical aids to calculation which we have learned in the book so far.

1 (section 1.4). Calculations involving sums and powers of numbers can often be shortened to involve only a few key strokes if we master the use of the automatic K constant operations.

2 (section 1.6). The principles of commutativity and associativity of multiplication say that we can multiply numbers in any order to get their product. For example

$$abc = acb.$$

By changing the order of terms carefully we can sometimes avoid overflow happening part way through the calculation (particularly if the calculator does not use scientific notation).

3 (section 1.6). On a non-scientific calculator we can still handle very large and very small numbers if we take out the powers of 10 from the numbers and treat them using the law of exponents. Further, multiplying or dividing a decimal number by powers of 10 simply involves moving the decimal point to the right or left by the appropriate number of places.

4 (section 1.6). We can check whether the calculator is telling 'the whole truth' in simple calculations by using the rule for the number of decimal places in a product.

5 (section 2.4). We know how to estimate errors in simple multiplication and division when we have some idea of the errors in the factors involved.

6 (section 2.9). The area of a rectangle is given by the product (length × width). By looking at the diagram below we see that

Total area = area 1 + area 2

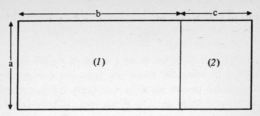

In mathematical notation this gives us the result

$a(b+c) = (ab)+(ac)$.

This is the distributive law, and it is one which we often use in mental arithmetic. For example, we work out 3×97 as $3 \times (100-3)$ $= 300-9 = 291$. Alternatively, we could work it out as $(3 \times 90)+$ (3×7), which would amount to doing the usual form of 'long multiplication'.

3.2. Sums of products (for S.A.L. calculators)

In order to calculate the floor area of an L-shaped room, we must work out the area of the various rectangular pieces and add them together. This means that we have to work out sums of products of the form $ab+cd$. If the calculator has a memory, we can work out ab, put it in the memory, and then work out cd. The last step is then to add the stored value of (ab) to the value of (cd) which is in the display. For an S.A.L. (algebraic logic) calculator with ⟦MS⟧ (memory store) and ⟦MR⟧ (memory recall) keys the key stroke sequence would be

⟦$a \times b =$ MS $c \times d +$ MR $=$⟧

If the calculator has an ⟦M+⟧ key, the result (cd) can be added into the memory, but we must be careful only to use ⟦M+⟧ to put the initial product (ab) into the memory if the memory is clear (which it will not be if we have been using it in a previous calculation). To store (ab) it is safer to use ⟦MS⟧; by making this a definite rule we avoid the possibility of error. On an A.O.S.

calculator, of course, the key strokes $a \times b + c \times d$ suffice to work out $(a \times b) + (c \times d)$, but we restrict ourselves to S.A.L. machines in sections 3.2 and 3.3.

If the calculator does *not* have a memory we do not have to write down (ab) while we work out (cd), but can perform the whole calculation in one piece by modifying the distributive law given in the preceding section. (This trick is also useful if the calculator memory is already holding some important number which must be kept for a later calculation.) The distributive law can be written 'backwards' as

$$ab + ac = (b + c)a.$$

It tells us how to add ac to ab, whereas we actually want to add cd to ab. If we could replace cd by 'a times something' we could do the calculation. The 'something' required can be called z, and we thus require that

$$cd = az,$$

which gives us the result

$$z = cd \div a.$$

Putting all the pieces together again we have the result

$$
\begin{aligned}
ab + cd &= ab + az \\
&= (b + z)a \\
&= \left(\frac{cd}{a} + b\right)a.
\end{aligned}
$$

Working this out 'by eye' we can see that the quantity cd is first divided by a and later multiplied by a, so that it emerges unscathed (apart from a possible small rounding error). This trick of multiplying and dividing by the same number has already been explained in section 1.7 as a device for correcting a false entry into the keyboard if the calculator has no $[\![CE]\!]$ key. The key strokes for working out $ab + cd$ can be read out from the formula just obtained as

$$[\![c \times d \div a + b \times a =]\!].$$

We note that there is a kind of symmetry in the formula, caused by the fact that $ab = ba$ – the commutative law; if we exchange a and b we are working out the *same number*. However, there *is* a difference as far as the calculator operator is concerned, since if he exchanges a and b he must enter b twice instead of entering a twice. If, for example, $a = 2$ and $b = 3.794821$, it takes seventeen key strokes to enter a once and b twice and nine key strokes to enter b once and a twice. Indeed, if any one of the four numbers a, b, c, d is much shorter than the others, it will be most economical to use it in the a position in the key stroke sequence. This kind of tactical planning becomes second nature to a calculator user once he has gained experience (provided, of course, that he has been gently encouraged to think critically about his calculations). The main thing is to keep a sense of proportion; calculator users who do not have a highly developed sense of 'cunning' sometimes feel more confident if they stick to a fool-proof rigid sequence of key strokes which works, even if it is sometimes a little less efficient than another sequence which would involve the operator making more decisions during the calculation. Even in the world of science there is a tendency to use standard fixed library programs to do certain routine calculations, since tinkering with them to make them slightly better for the particular data concerned is regarded as being too costly in time and effort.

3.3. Products of sums

Suppose that we measure the dimensions of a large room by using a broken measure only 2.47 metres long. We have to mark where the end of the measure falls and then start again.

The dimensions of the room might be, say, $(2.47 + 1.31)$ and $(2.47 + 0.71)$. To work out the area essentially involves evaluating a product of sums of the type

$$(a+b)(c+d).$$

At first sight it seems difficult to work this out without using a memory to hold $(c+d)$ while we work out $(a+b)$. Indeed in one book on the use of calculators the author says that there does not seem to be a way to avoid use of a memory if we use algebraic logic. However, we *can* do the trick if we use a little logical thought to build on what we already know. We know how to work out sums of products from the discussion given in the preceding section. The quantity which we want can be written as

$$(a+b)c + (a+b)d,$$

which is a sum of products. The only difference between this case and the one we discussed previously is that the names have been changed round. Thus, $(a+b)$ plays the role of a and of c, while c plays the role of b. Making these appropriate changes in our formula for the sum of products (from the preceding section) we obtain the result

$$\left[\frac{(a+b)d}{c} + a + b\right]c$$

or (in key strokes)

$$[\![a\ +\ b\ \times\ d\ \div\ c\ +\ a\ +\ b\ \times\ c\ =]\!]$$

The present author must admit that he finds the above formula to be a borderline case; it involves entering seven numbers and it may well be more easy and speedy to jot down $(a+b)$ on paper and then multiply it by $(c+d)$. It seems that our algebraic ingenuity has here reached a point at which diminishing returns are setting in, and we must be wise enough to know when to give in gracefully. If we regard the calculator plus the human operator plus his notebook as 'the computer', it is clear that somewhere in the system must be held the numbers a, b, c, d, which we used as the raw data for our calculations in the preceding two sections. They are not in the calculator (if it has no memories), so they are in some other memory, that is, in the notebook. The operator's head provides short-term memory, of course, but it is unlikely to be handling four decimal numbers at a time. Given that the notebook is in use already, it may be that the 'crude' method which uses the notebook is sometimes as useful as a more clever method which involves formulae as lengthy as our one for a product of sums. If necessary, then, we must be prepared to use the slow-speed memory of the 'computer' (pad and pencil) if it turns out to give us a short or fool-proof route to the required result. For our starting example most readers would probably trust the human part of the computer (their head) to work out $2.47 + 1.31 = 3.78$ mentally before using the calculator, but the numbers aren't always so simple!

In this and the preceding section we have studied how to break down a calculation into a sequence of operations suitable for a simple S.A.L. machine. On a calculator with brackets we can get a sum of products by using the key strokes

$$[a \times b + (c \times d) =].$$

However on some calculators (e.g., the CBM 899D) the bracketed quantity $(c \times d)$ is kept in the calculator memory, that is, the brackets keys actually activate the same memory as the memory keys. If we have some number in the memory which we wish to keep we must avoid using the bracket key, since $(c \times d)$ will destroy the previous memory contents.

3.4. Square and cube roots

In our discussion so far we have supposed that the simple calculator which we are using has a square root key $[\sqrt{\ }]$. If we have a square root key it is easy to find the square root of any number y. We use the key strokes $[y \ \sqrt{\ }]$. If we have *no* square root key we can try a 'trial and error' method, but one of the systematic methods of finding square roots, which we will now describe, goes back to the ancient Greeks (as do lots of interesting ideas about numbers). Suppose we want the square root of y, and call this number x. We can write down the definition of x in several ways:

$$x = \sqrt{y}$$
$$x^2 = y$$
$$x = \frac{y}{x}.$$

It is the third equation which turns out to be the useful one. If we *guess* a value x_0 for x, and then divide y by x_0, we shall get x_0 again if we guessed right. However, if our guess x_0 was too big, $y \div x_0$ will be too small, and vice-versa. A common-sense approach would be to say 'let us take an average', and it turns out that is precisely what a more careful mathematical argument tells us to do. (The common-sense approach is not quite so successful for the cube root problem, as we shall see.) Taking our guess x_0, which will be, say, larger than x, and our ratio $y \div x_0$, which will be smaller than x, we work out the average

$$x_1 = \frac{1}{2}\left(\frac{y}{x_0} + x_0\right).$$

Now, having got x_1, we can use x_1 in the formula to work out a further number

$$x_2 = \frac{1}{2}\left(\frac{y}{x_1} + x_1\right)$$

and so on. This is what mathematicians call an *iterative* process (one involving repetitions of the same calculation). The beauty of modern calculators and computers is that they enable the repetitive calculations to be done quickly, and in modern applied mathematics iterative methods are used in areas where years ago they would have been regarded as very tedious. Using an S.A.L. calculator with a memory and automatic K constant, we can work out x_1 with the following key strokes (if x_0 is first placed in the memory):

$$[y \div MR + MR \div 2 = MS].$$

These strokes leave x_1 in the memory and in the display. Putting y in the display again, we can use the same cycle of key strokes to get x_2, x_3, etc. If we set $y = 2$ as a simple example, and take $x_0 = 1.5$ as our first guess for $\sqrt{2}$, we get the successive results

$x_1 = 1.4166666$
$x_2 = 1.4142156$
$x_3 = 1.4142135$
$x_4 = 1.4142135.$

We see that x_3 is (to our eight-figure accuracy) $\sqrt{2}$, since x_4 simply reproduces it. Further, the numbers x_1, x_2, and so on rapidly get nearer to $\sqrt{2}$ with each cycle of calculation (in mathematical jargon the iterative process *converges*).

The calculator shows us that the method works in practice, and for many calculator users this is sufficient. However, we would like to see *why* it works; this will teach us some mathematics, and what we learn will be of practical use when we deal with cube roots. We can make a general observation here: to know *that* a thing works is sufficient in given circumstances, but to deal with *changing* circumstances we usually need some theoretical knowledge of *why* it works. In short, theory is often eminently practical! Now, suppose that our first guess x_0 is greater than x (i.e., $\sqrt{y}$). We represent this by using the equation

$$x_0 = x + h$$

where h, the error of our guess, is greater than zero. What we work out next is $y \div x_0$, with x_0 equal to $x + h$. We assert that

$$\frac{y}{x+h} = x - h + \frac{h^2}{x+h}$$

and can *prove* this by multiplying on both left and right by $x + h$. On the left we get y, on the right we get

$$(x+h)(x-h) + h^2 = x^2 - h^2 + h^2$$

which is also y, since $x^2 = y$. We used here a general principle: multiplying a true (or false) equation throughout by the same non-zero number gives another true (or false) equation. Note that a non-zero number must be used; multiplying the false equation $5 = 7$ on both sides by zero gives the true equation $0 = 0$. We can now work out the averaged quantity $\frac{1}{2}(y/x_0) + \frac{1}{2}x_0$, which we called x_1. We find

$$x_1 = \frac{1}{2}\left(x + h + x - h + \frac{h^2}{x+h}\right)$$
$$= x + \frac{1}{2}\frac{h^2}{(x+h)}.$$

We see that the averaging process causes the terms involving h to the first power to vanish. Suppose that we look at the *fractional error* (h/x), in the guess x_0. The fractional error in the new number x_1 is equal to $(x_1 - x) \div x$, which is

$$\frac{1}{2}h^2 \frac{1}{x(x+h)}.$$

If h is sufficiently small, this fractional error is very close to the value

$$\frac{1}{2}\frac{h^2}{y} = \frac{1}{2}\left(\frac{h}{\sqrt{y}}\right)^2$$

i.e. it is equal to half of the square of the fractional error in x_0. It is clear that similar arguments hold on passing from x_1 to x_2, and so on. As a numerical test of this prediction, we can look at the fractional errors arising at successive stages of our calculation of $\sqrt{2}$. The results were given earlier, and using them we find the following successive fractional errors:

0.06066, 0.00173, 0.00000148.

Our simple rule, starting from the initial fractional error 0.06066, would have predicted the next two fractional errors to be 0.00184 and 0.0000016, which fits quite well to our actual calculated results.

If our calculator has a square root key, we can find cube roots by the method described in Chapter 2, but we can also find cube roots by another method. If we denote the cube root of y by x, we can take the equation

$$x = \frac{y}{x^2}$$

as our definition of x, and can then proceed as for the square root. If we try the averaging process, as before, we will start from a first guess x_0 and calculate

$$x_1 = \frac{1}{2}\frac{y}{x_0^2} + \frac{1}{2}x_0.$$

Suppose we take $y = 8$, so that we know the exact result is $\sqrt[3]{8} = 2$. We get the following sequences of numbers starting from $x_0 = 2.2$:

1.9264462, 2.041043, 1.9807081, 2.0099287...

This shows the kind of effect we are looking for, but the process is working much less quickly than it did for our square root calculation. In fact, it is the simple averaging which is wrong –

we should use what in statistics is called a *weighted average* (in fact a mixture of 2 parts to 1):

$$x_1 = \tfrac{1}{3}\left(\frac{y}{x_0^2} + 2x_0\right).$$

To see why, we pretend (as before) that we have $x_0 = x + h$, and find

$$\frac{y}{(x+h)^2} = \frac{y}{x^2} \frac{1}{(1+z)^2}$$

where we use the shorthand symbol y for the ratio (h/x). We can work out the product

$$(1+z)^2(1-2z) = 1 - 3z^2 - 2z^3.$$

This product is almost exactly 1 for very small y, so that the reciprocal of $(1+y)^2$ can be taken to be $(1-2y)$. Putting together the two parts which make up x_1, we find

$$x_1 = \frac{1}{3}.\frac{y}{x^2}(1-2z) + \frac{2}{3}(x+h)$$

$$= x + \text{no term in } h \; (+\text{correction terms}).$$

(To get this last result we remember that $y = x^3$ and $h = xz$.) Thus we have got rid of the h terms, just as we did with the square root formula; the correction terms mentioned involve h^2 and higher powers, and are not given in detail by this simple approach. Using a simple calculator, the sequence for working out x_1 (with x_0 in the memory) is

$$[\![y \div \mathrm{MR} = = + \mathrm{MR} = = \div 3 = \mathrm{MS}]\!]$$

on an S.A.L. machine with memory and automatic K constant. Taking the case $y = 8$ again, we get a much more speedy process than before: with $x_0 = 2.2$ we get the estimates (2.2, 2.0176308, 2.0001536, 2 exactly). The process of 'making the h terms vanish' which we have used here can be used to construct iterative formulae for fourth, fifth and higher roots. (Exercise 4 gives a further discussion.)

3.5. Numbers near to one

By taking the square roots and the reciprocals of many numbers close to 1 (e.g., $\sqrt{1.05} = 1.0247$, $1.05^{-1} = 0.9524$) the reader should discover a certain regularity, which can be summarized by the equations

$$(1+x)^{\frac{1}{2}} \simeq 1+\tfrac{1}{2}x$$
$$(1+x)^{-1} \simeq 1-x$$

where $\simeq$ means 'is approximately equal to'. As x gets smaller these two equations become more and more accurate. In Chapter 1 we saw that the notation for powers of numbers is designed to obey the simple law of exponents, but we can see that the notation *also* gives us a rule for finding powers of numbers near to 1. If we 'take the hint' from the cases of the square root and the reciprocal, for which most calculators have a key, then for the case of a cube root (where we do not have a key) we might guess that the law for cube roots of numbers near to 1 is

$$(1+x)^{\frac{1}{3}} \simeq 1+\tfrac{1}{3}x$$

and trying this out on a few numbers shows that it is the appropriate formula. Now, how would we *prove* what the preceding results lead us to suspect? Well, even if we cannot see how to do it, we can always do the next best thing and show that it works. So, for example, we know that $(1+x)^{\frac{1}{3}}$ means 'cube root of $1+x$', which means that we must have (for small x values)

$$(1+\tfrac{1}{3}x)(1+\tfrac{1}{3}x)(1+\tfrac{1}{3}x) = (1+x)$$

if our conjecture is correct. To work out the left-hand side, a product of three sums, we use the same process as explained in section 3.1 for the area of the rectangular shape, that is, we convert it into a sum of products. We get for the square

$$(1+\tfrac{1}{3}x)(1+\tfrac{1}{3}x) = 1+\tfrac{2}{3}x+(\tfrac{1}{3}x)^2$$

and, multiplying this by $(1+\tfrac{1}{3}x)$ again, to get the cube, gives

$$(1+\tfrac{1}{3}x)^3 = 1+x+3(\tfrac{1}{3}x)^2+3(\tfrac{1}{3}x)^3.$$

If x is small (say $\frac{1}{10}$), the terms involving x^2 and x^3 are much smaller than x, and so it is a good approximation to put

$$(1 + \tfrac{1}{3}x)^3 = 1 + x.$$

But this is a 'backwards' way of saying that $(1 + \tfrac{1}{3}x)$ is the cube root of $1 + x$!

For reciprocals we can be even more detailed. We know that

$$1 = (1 + x) - x.$$

This seems a silly equation, but there is method in the madness, as we shall see! Dividing *both* sides of the equation by $(1 + x)$ still leaves an equation, which is

$$(1 + x)^{-1} = 1 - x(1 + x)^{-1}.$$

If we use the separate symbol r (for reciprocal) for $(1 + x)^{-1}$ the equation is

$$r = 1 - xr.$$

Now, if x is small $(1 + x)^{-1}$ will be close to 1. If we put this estimate into the right-hand side of our equation we get

$$r \simeq 1 - x.$$

If we then put *this* approximation into the right-hand side of our equation for r we get

$$r \simeq 1 - x(1 - x) = 1 - x + x^2$$

and so on, that is, we have an *iterative* process, of the kind mentioned earlier (in the square root calculation). For the reciprocal then, we can go beyond the x type term, and we have here the beginning ideas of the *binomial theorem*, which tells us how to get these extra correction terms for $(1 + x)^n$, with n any number. Although we do not use the general theorem in this book, we can easily work out the cases $n = 2, 3$, directly. For example,
$$(1 + x)^2 = (1 + x)(1 + x) = 1 + 2x + x^2.$$

This simple result for the square will turn out to be very powerful in some of our work in Chapter 3.

The method for finding cube roots which we explained in section

3.4 has one obvious disadvantage: during each cycle of the iteration process the number y (for which we need $y^{\frac{1}{3}}$) is destroyed, and must be entered again. This will mean that we shall have to write it down on a note-pad which is external to the machine. If we want to avoid this re-entering, we can get a good approximate value for $y^{\frac{1}{3}}$ as follows. We proceed by means of a numerical example.

Suppose we want $(9.23)^{\frac{1}{3}}$. We 'scale down' the 9.23 by repeatedly taking the square root (using the square root key). Thus

$(9.23) \rightarrow 1.0010857$ (eleven square roots).

Now we *can* find the cube root of a number close to 1; we put

$$(1.0010857)^{\frac{1}{3}} = 1 + \tfrac{1}{3}(0.0010857)$$
$$= \tfrac{1}{3}(2 + 1.0010857)$$
$$= 1.0003619.$$

(The second equation above is included to show how to calculate the result briefly on a calculator. Starting from the display 1.0010857 we only press the keys $[\![+ \ 2 \ \div \ 3]\!]$, whereas we need the key strokes $[\![- \ 1 \ \div \ 3 \ + \ 1]\!]$ if we use the approach suggested by the first equation.) Now we 'scale up' the number to its original size, that is, we square it eleven times (to undo the eleven square roots). We get

$(1.0003619) \rightarrow 2.0980$ (eleven squarings).

The cube root of 9.23 is actually 2.0977 to four figures. We thus have a method which seems to be about as accurate as the four-place logarithms which are used in schools. We see, then, that by learning about powers of numbers near to 1 we can (again!) use the square root key on the calculator to work out cube roots. Not only that, once we understand the process, we can use it to get fifth roots, sixth roots, etc.! We just divide by 5 (or 6) instead of 3 at the middle step of the calculation. (To get fourth roots, of course, we just press the square root key twice!) There is one feature of the method which requires some judgement: how many times should we take the square root? We used 11 square roots. In fact, it is here that we can do experiments with the calculator. We take some number, 8, say, for which we know the cube root (2), and see what happens if we take 8, 9, 10, 11 square roots and so on, in the process outlined above. We find (quoting the final result to only four figures):

(9 roots) $8 \rightarrow 1.0040696 \rightarrow 2.0018$
(10 roots) $8 \rightarrow 1.0020327 \rightarrow 2.0007$
(11 roots) $8 \rightarrow 1.0010158 \rightarrow 2.0002$
(12 roots) $8 \rightarrow 1.0005077 \rightarrow 1.9994$

From this and other trial calculations we get the 'rule of thumb' that the intermediate number should be between 1.001 and 1.002 to give the best results. We need to get close to 1 to use our simple result for the cube root, but if we go below 1.001 we only get four figures instead of five at the end of the number, which makes us lose accuracy. We shall use this process of scaling down and then scaling up again in several of our calculations in Chapter 3. Indeed it serves to make the square root key a much more powerful weapon than we could guess just by looking at its basic function!

3.6. Calculator 'stretching'

The simple result for the square of the sum of two numbers is

$$(x+y)^2 = x^2 + 2xy + y^2.$$

To see how even such an innocent-looking equation can lead to surprising results, we will show how to use it to 'stretch' the display length of an eight-figure calculator; we will, in particular, calculate $\sqrt{2}$ to eleven decimal places! Our first step is to remember the principle stated in Chapter 1 for finding the number of decimal places in a product. If we start with 1.414, an approximation to $\sqrt{2}$, we know that squaring it gives a number which can be completely displayed (without chopping the end off) in an eight-figure display. We find $(1.414)^2 = 1.999396$. Thus the correct value of $\sqrt{2}$ is a little larger than 1.414. We will call it $1.414+h$, where the error h is what we need to know. We know that the following equations must hold:

$$2 = (\sqrt{2})^2 = (1.414+h)^2$$
$$= (1.414)^2 + 2(1.414h) + h^2$$
$$= 1.999396 + 2.828h + h^2.$$

It follows that

$$2 - 1.999396 = 0.000604 = h(2.828 + h),$$

that is,

$$h = \frac{0.000604}{(2.828 + h)}.$$

h is very small, so we try putting $h = 0$ on the right as a first estimate. We get 0.00021357 if we directly set $[\![0.000604 \div 2.828]\!]$ in the calculator. To be clever we remember that multiplying (or dividing) by 10 simply moves the decimal point along the number, and we use 604 instead of 0.000604, putting back the point to its correct place afterwards. This gives us the better result

$$\frac{0.000604}{2.828} = 0.0002135785$$

for our estimate of h. Now we put this h value into the calculation again (an iterative process again!) and find for our second estimate of h:

$$\frac{0.000604}{2.8282135[785]} = 0.00021356237.$$

We show the three numbers [785] in a square bracket because we cannot enter them in our eight-figure calculator, but stop at the 5 which precedes them. This does not change the answer. How do we know? Well, we use 6 instead of 5 as this last digit, and see that the same result comes out. (If a big kick will not move it, a little nudge certainly will not!) It follows that we have got our h value as well as we can, and we conclude that

$$\sqrt{2} = 1.414 + h$$
$$= 1.41421356237,$$

which has four more figures than we get by using the square root key directly. Indeed, if you check through the calculation you will see that a square root key has not been used (although if we had one it would have given us the 1.414 as our first estimate, otherwise we could use trial and error to find it). The reader may amuse himself by showing that $\sqrt{3} = 1.73205080757\ldots$

3.7. Change of base

In Chapter 1 we explained the way in which a number can be expressed to base 5 or base 10, and now we see how to express an integer in any basis. We can explain best by using an example. We take the number 735 (in base 10, of course) and try to write it using the base 6. First we proceed as follows (on an automatic K constant machine):

$$[\![735 \div 6 = = =]\!] \quad \boxed{3.4027776} \qquad (3)$$

stopping as soon as the result is less than 6. Next, we remove the 3, and multiply by 6,

$$[\![- 3 \times 6 =]\!] \quad \boxed{2.4166656}. \qquad (2)$$

Remove the 2, multiply by 6,

$$[\![- 2 \times 6 =]\!] \quad \boxed{2.4999936}. \qquad (2)$$

Remove the 2, multiply by 6,

$$[\![- 2 \times 6 =]\!] \quad \boxed{2.9999616}. \qquad (3)$$

We stop here, since this last result is obviously the calculator's attempt to give us a 3, but has been frustrated by rounding errors. We now tot up the 'cast-off' integers which we have shown in a bracket at each stage, and set the result down as

$$(735)_{10} = (3223)_6.$$

A human operator using this process can recognize how to get rid of the integers at each stage, and also when to allow for rounding at the last stage. To program some types of programmable calculator to make these decisions would be quite difficult, so here is one case where the human brain comes out ahead! To see how the calculation works we can set it out as follows:

$$735 = (3 \times 6^3) + (2 \times 6^2) + (2 \times 6^1) + (3 \times 6^0)$$
$$\frac{735}{6^3} = 3 + (2 \times 6^{-1}) + (2 \times 6^{-2}) + (3 \times 6^{-3})$$
$$6[(2 \times 6^{-1}) + (2 \times 6^{-2}) + (3 \times 6^{-3})] = 2 + (2 \times 6^{-1}) + (3 \times 6^{-2})$$

and so on. At each stage we 'peel off' one of the integers needed in the final result. (Note that we count zero as an integer! For example, $7_{10} = 101_6$, so we obtain a zero in our list of 'cast-off' integers.)

3.8. Nested multiplication

In treating various problems of applied mathematics it is necessary to work out *polynomials*, that is, expressions involving sums of powers of a number. Using the symbol x as the name for a number, an example of a polynomial is the simple expression:

$2x^2 + 3x + 5.$

To work this out on a calculator with a memory we might think of working out $2x^2$, then $3x$, then 5, and adding them. Unfortunately, we cannot keep x and $2x^2$ in the memory at the same time, and would need to enter x more than once. The *nested multiplication* procedure splits the expression as follows:

$(2x + 3)x + 5.$

If we put x in the display, and also have a memory available, we can work the nested expression out directly using the key strokes

$[\![MS \times 2 + 3 \times MR + 5 =]\!]$

(At $x = 1$ we should get 10; try it and see!)

What if we do not have a memory (in the calculator, that is!)? We have to think a bit harder, but can manage to write the expression as follows:

$\frac{1}{8}[(4x + 3)^2 + 31] = 2x^2 + 3x + 5.$

To see this, use the expression given earlier for the square of a sum, or check that it is correct directly, by *working it out* for trial values such as $x = 0, 1$, etc., noting that it always gives the same answer as $2x^2 + 3x + 5$. (This simple-minded method is often useful even in advanced scientific work.) To work out $2x^2 + 3x + 5$ using the last expression we only need to enter the number x once, provided that we can work out the square of a number on our calculator (either with an $[\![x^2]\!]$ key or the key strokes $[\![\times \ =]\!]$). With a little experience, an operator will be able to convert any polynomial involving x^2 and x into this 'single entry' form.

As a simple example of a nested multiplication we can work out the number $(3223)_6$ from the previous section, that is, change it to scale 10. We have a nested multiplication, with 6 playing the role of x:

$$\begin{aligned}(3223)_6 &= (3 \times 6^3) + (2 \times 6^2) + (2 \times 6) + 3\\ &= [(3 \times 6 + 2)6 + 2]6 + 3\\ &= 735.\end{aligned}$$

This can be worked out by entering 6 only once if we have a memory:

$$[6 \text{ MS} \times 3 + 2 \times \text{MR} + 2 \times \text{MR} + 3 =]$$

As a further example, the reader may verify that $1010101_2 = 85_{10}$.

3.9. More 'stretching'. Rational numbers

The stretching process which we used for $\sqrt{2}$ in section 3.6 can be employed with even more success for reciprocals. We treat $\frac{1}{7}$ (i.e., 7^{-1}) as an example. We work out $1 \div 7$ on the calculator, and get

$$\tfrac{1}{7} = 0.1428571.$$

Now 7×7^{-1} should equal 1, but the calculator actually gives

$$7(0.1428571) = 0.9999997.$$

Let us suppose that $7^{-1} = 0.1428571 + h$. We have

$$1 = 7(0.1428571 + h) = 0.9999997 + 7h.$$

This leads to the result

$$h = \tfrac{0.0000003}{7}.$$

If we put this into the calculator we get zero, because the answer is too small to show using only eight figures. However, we work out $3 \div 7$ instead, and put the decimal point in the right place afterwards. This gives us the result for 7^{-1}.

$$\tfrac{1}{7} = 0.14285714285714,$$

to fourteen decimal places! (Warning: these particular figures are for a CBM 899D machine; other machines may give 28 on the end as well, with slightly different numbers throughout the calculation.) It seems that the figures in the decimal show a repetitive behaviour, with the sequence 142857 being repeated. We have here an illustration of a result from the simple theory of numbers: the decimal form of a rational number *either repeats* (like 7^{-1}) or *terminates* (like $5^{-1} = 0.02000$). A *rational number* is a ratio of two integers (i.e., whole numbers, 1, 2, 3, etc.). A number such as $\sqrt{2}$, which we examined previously, is *irrational*, that is, there are no two integers which have a ratio of $\sqrt{2}$. The proof of this goes back (again!) at least to the ancient Greeks, and we can discern no repetition in the decimal form of $\sqrt{2}$ as we obtained it earlier. Of course, if the basic block of numbers which repeats is too long we will not be able to spot it even by our stretching process. We can actually do a super-stretch in some cases. For 7^{-1} we have, from our preceding discussion,

$$h = \frac{0.0000003}{7} = (0.0000003)7^{-1}$$
$$h = (0.0000003)(0.1428571 + h).$$

Now, we have an iterative process again! We use $h = 0$ on the right as first approximation, and get out on the left the result for 7^{-1} which we have quoted to fourteen places previously. If we go on putting in improved h estimates on the right, we get more and more figures in our result. The reader can check that these longer and longer numbers simply repeat the sequence 142857.

3.10. More repeating decimals

We have just seen how to convert the fraction $\frac{1}{7}$ into a repeating decimal, but we can also consider how to find which fraction is represented by a repeating decimal. Suppose we have the number 1.232323... with the 23 digits repeating. We put this in the calculator (which obviously can't take *all* of the numbers!), and keep on multiplying by 10 until we get 'something point 23'.

$[\![1.2323232 \times 10 = =]\!]$ $\boxed{123.23232}$.

Now we subtract the starting number (which we could keep in the memory),

$$[- \; 1.2323232 \; =] \quad \boxed{122}.$$

This last result *must* be a whole number, because we have deliberately 'lined up' the 23 pairs in the two numbers being subtracted. We know that they *all* cancel, even the ones right off the end of the calculator display. The result 122 was obtained by working out $100 \times 1.2323\ldots$ and then subtracting $1.2323\ldots$, and so must be equal to $99 \times 1.2323\ldots$ We then have the result

$$1.2323\ldots = \frac{122}{99}$$

and verify it (S.I.A.S.!) by working out $122 \div 99$ on the calculator.

A number which *appears* to be a repeating decimal is e, the base of natural logarithms. It is often quoted as

$$e = 2.718281828$$

and it appears that the 1828 portion repeats. It doesn't; the next digit is a 4, as is shown by scientific calculators which work to many decimal places. If we treat the truncated form of e shown above as a repeating decimal we get the digits to line up after multiplying by 10^4 and find for our 'repeating e' the result

$$
\begin{aligned}
10^4 e &= 27182.81828\ldots \\
e &= 2.71828\ldots \\
9999 e &= 27180.1
\end{aligned}
$$

i.e., e (repeating) $= \dfrac{271801}{99990}$

if we put back a factor of 10 in the two numbers. The reader can do this division to see that it does indeed give the correct result.

We have spoken of repeating *decimals* so far, but repeating digits can also occur when numbers are expressed using bases other than 10. For example, if we use the method explained in section 3.7 to convert the number $(2.1)_{10}$ to binary form, with base 2, we end up with the result

$$(10.00011001100\ldots)_2 = (2.1)_{10}.$$

The digits 1100 repeat in this binary form. Manipulating numbers using different bases gradually encourages us to think of numbers as 'things in themselves', the decimal or binary or octal forms of a number being various representations or names for the underlying entity. This notion of having different representations of some underlying more abstract entity plays an important role in advanced theories which deal with group theory and tensor analysis. To 'work out' a repeating binary number of the type just given above we can proceed as for the decimal case, but must remember that moving the digits along by one place corresponds to dividing (or multiplying) by 2 and not 10. It is easy to give a decimal translation alongside the binary numbers:

$$100001.1001100\ldots \qquad , \quad 16x$$
$$10.0001100\ldots \qquad , \quad x$$

Difference: $(32 + 1 + \frac{1}{2}) - 2 = 31\frac{1}{2}$, $15x$.

This gives (in decimal), $x = \dfrac{63}{30}$, i.e. 2.1.

The interesting feature here is that we can work out $16x - x$ *before* knowing x as a fraction, since we have used the lining up of the digits to simplify the subtraction.

We can use repeating decimals to teach us something about geometric series. For example, if we remember how to use powers of 10 we can write the repeating decimal which we treated at the start of this section as

$$1.2323 = 1 + 23(10^{-2} + 10^{-4} + 10^{-6} + \ldots)$$

where the negative powers of 10 go on 'for ever'.

We have already established that the repeating decimal represents the fraction $122 \div 99$, which is $1 + (23 \div 99)$, and so we conclude that

$$\frac{1}{99} = (10^{-2} + 10^{-4} + 10^{-6} + \ldots)$$

i.e., the infinite series on the right does not grow for ever, but settles down to a definite sum. The series on the right is called a *geometric series*, and it has the property that the $(n+1)$th term is equal to a fixed constant r times the nth term. For our example the *common ratio* r is equal to 10^{-2}, because we started from a repeating decimal in which the repeating unit is a block of two digits. We can devise an argument for finding the sum of an infinite geometric series by the following trick. If we *suppose* that the sum is s we set

$$s = a + ar + ar^2 + \ldots = a(1 + r + r^2 + \ldots)$$

and so have to find the sum only for the special case $a = 1$ (since we can insert the correct a multiplying factor afterwards). We then have (at $a = 1$)

$$s = 1 + r + r^2 + \ldots = 1 + r(1 + r + \ldots)$$
$$= 1 + rs.$$

Here the same series appears twice in the equation! We can now work out the result:

$$s = \frac{1}{(1-r)} = (1-r)^{-1}$$

which becomes $a(1-r)^{-1}$ if the first term in the series is a rather than 1. We have shown that *if* the definite sum exists it must have the value $a(1-r)^{-1}$; applying the result to our special case above gives $a = r = 10^{-2}$, so that

$$s = \frac{10^{-2}}{1 - 10^{-2}} = \frac{1}{99}.$$

If we look at the geometric series and make r greater than 1 it is clear that there is no definite number s to which the sum will settle down as more terms are added. If we take $r = 2$, for example, without remembering the details of our calculation, we would apparently conclude that

$$1 + 2 + 4 + 8 + \ldots = -1.$$

Using $r = -2$ would give the result

$$1 - 2 + 4 - 8 + \ldots = \tfrac{1}{3}.$$

These two results would be classed as nonsense for the kind of problems considered in this book. In some advanced parts of theoretical physics, however, it does sometimes happen that a calculation which has been carried out using infinite series will yield a 'silly' series (like our series for $r = -2$). If we know sufficient about the theory of infinite series it is sometimes possible to see that the true answer should be, say, $\frac{1}{3}$, as given by the simple formula; the mathematics then has to be interpreted as telling us that the infinite series method is a poor way of doing the calculation. ('Can you tell me the way to Dorchester?' – 'Why sir, if I were going there I wouldn't start from here!')

3.11. Lenses and lighthouses

If a source of light is placed at a point which is at a distance u from a thin convex lens, the light rays passing through the lens will be refracted so as to produce an image of the source:

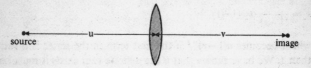

The image distance v is given by a formula which involves reciprocals,

$$\frac{1}{u} + \frac{1}{v} = \frac{1}{f}$$

The number f depends on the detailed shape of the lens and is called the focal length of the lens. If we use the lens as a burning glass to focus the sun's rays into a bright spot, the rays focus at distance f from the lens. To see this, we set u in the formula equal to a very large number (the distance from the sun to the earth) and note that $1/u$ is then very small indeed. This means that v becomes equal to f (with a negligible error), and so we can find f from the 'burning glass' experiment. Having found f, we can use it to estimate the image position for sources at varying distances u. If u is less than f, then $1/u$ will be greater than $1/f$. This means that to obey the formula v must be a negative number. It looks as though we cannot show such a negative number in our diagram, since all the v values on the image side of the lens are positive numbers. The negative v *can* be interpreted, however, if we think of the formula as telling us at what point the rays bent by the lens come together. A value of $v = -8$ cm tells us that the lens has not bent the rays sufficiently to turn them inwards; instead, they are spreading outwards as though they had come *from* a point 8 cm on the source side of the lens, instead of from the true source point.

One interesting feature of the *thin lens formula* (as it is called) is the symmetry between u and v which it shows. If u and v are interchanged the equation is still obeyed; this is a mathematical expression of the principle that the path of the light rays is reversible. If a light source is placed at distance f from the lens (described by setting $u = f$ in the formula) the result is a parallel beam of light (described by the result $1/v = 0$, i.e., $v =$ infinity). This is the reverse of the situation which is present in the burning glass experiment. A lighthouse has a lens system which operates roughly in this way, and it is sometimes necessary to shield the lens by curtains on sunny days to prevent the sun's rays coming to focus on the lamp apparatus and starting a fire. This interesting example of reversibility was discovered by the author on a visit to the Strumble Head lighthouse near Fishguard in Wales.

The thin lens formula given above is usually known as *Newton's form* of the formula. A second version of the formula, *Gauss's form*, is as follows:

$$(u-f)(v-f) = f^2$$

and this form is useful when dealing with composite lenses made up of pairs of thin lenses (see exercise 14). That Gauss's form and Newton's form are identical mathematically (although not equally convenient) can be seen by noting that Newton's form gives the result $uv = f(u+v)$, which means that three of the terms in the expansion of $(u-f)(v-f)$ cancel, leaving only f^2.

3.12. Series and parallel resistors

Readers acquainted with simple electrical circuits will remember that the conventional symbol used to represent a battery with a resistance connected across it is

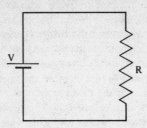

If a battery supplies V volts across the ends of a resistance of R ohms, the current which flows through the resistance is I amperes, where the formula relating the three quantities is

$$V = IR.$$

If two resistances, of r ohms and R ohms, are connected in series (i.e., end to end) they give a total resistance S, which is equal to $r + R$:

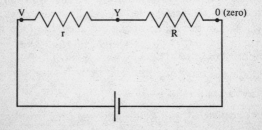

(The sign $\equiv$ means 'is equivalent to'.) The key to understanding this kind of result is to concentrate on the right variable (just as in section 2.10); here this variable is the *current*. If we imagine the voltage at various points to be as shown below we have the results

Current through $r = (V-Y) \div R$
Current through $R = (Y-0) \div R$.

However, the current through the two resistances will be the same if they are connected in series (this principle, that current cannot escape or pile up anywhere, is one of Kirchhoff's laws). If we call this current I, we must have the result

$$V = (V-Y)+Y$$
$$= Ir+IR = I(r+R),$$

where the distributive law has been used to obtain the last expression. Thus, the pair of resistances behaves like a single resistance $S = r+R$, since a voltage V applied to them produces a current $V \div (r+R)$.

Consider now two resistances in parallel:

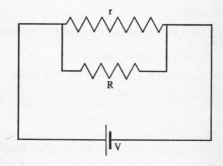

The current I round the circuit breaks up into two portions $I(r)$ and $I(R)$, which flow through r and R, respectively. As far as the battery is concerned the ratio $V \div I$ gives some apparent resistance P in the circuit. This means that we have the formula

$$I = I(r)+I(R)$$

which becomes

$$\frac{V}{P} = \frac{V}{r}+\frac{V}{R}.$$

We accordingly find

$$\frac{1}{P} = \frac{1}{r} + \frac{1}{R}$$

an equation involving reciprocals. We can work out P to obtain the result

$$P = \frac{rR}{(r+R)}.$$

We can represent the result symbolically as follows:

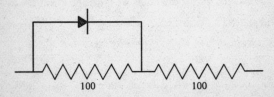

and our results can be represented in a simple mnemonic form:

*S*eries: *S*um; *P*arallel: *P*roduct over sum.

We also note that the following useful relation holds:

$SP = rR.$

A semiconductor diode has the property that it conducts current in one direction only; to be more accurate, it has a high resistance in one direction and a low resistance in the other. How could we use this property to make up a fixed resistor unit which has a resistance of 100 ohms or 200 ohms, depending on which way round its terminals are connected to a battery? One possible circuit (which could be made up into a single small component) is:

The diode symbol indicates that current can flow with the arrow, but not against it. If the battery tries to drive current from left to right, the diode acts as a very small resistance (i.e., roughly zero ohms). When connected across the 100 ohms the diode leads to a resistance which we can obtain using the formula for parallel resistance; it is zero in this case, and this zero produces a total resistance of 100 ohms when it is in series with the other 100 ohms. With the connections reversed the very high diode resistance connected across the 100 ohms gives a combined resistance very close to 100 ohms, so the whole circuit gives a resistance of 200 ohms (i.e., two 100-ohm resistors in series).

Ordinary pieces of metallic wire do not have the eccentric behaviour of the diode, but have the same resistance whichever way the current flows. If a piece of wire has a length l and an area of cross-section a, it has a resistance R which is proportional to l but *inversely* proportional to a. Using the proportion sign $\propto$ we can write

$$R \propto la^{-1}$$

– and note that being proportional to a^{-1} is the same as being inversely proportional to a. When a current I passes through the wire an amount of heat energy given by I^2R is produced per second in the wire. This heat leaks away by conduction, but if I gets too large the heat cannot get away fast enough and the wire melts; this is the way in which fuse wire acts. The centre of the wire will be the hottest point, since the heat produced there has to travel the farthest distance to leak away at the ends of the wire. According to our reasoning so far the amount of heat produced per second by the current I will be proportional to I^2R, i.e., proportional to $I^2l \div d^2$ if the wire is a circular one of diameter d. Thus the rate of heat production per centimetre at the centre is proportional to I^2d^{-2}. The rate of heat loss by conduction and radiation will also depend on d; if the loss were solely due to radiation from the hot wire surface it would be expected to be proportional to d, but the true dependence is probably not so simple, since the temperature varies across the wire. However, we might expect that the current I required to melt a piece of fuse wire (of given material) will depend on the diameter of the wire, perhaps according to some power law.

Indeed, if

$$I = kd^m$$

with k and m constants, it will follow that the ratio $I \div d^m$ will be equal to the constant k. One (S.I.A.S.!) approach is to test various m values to see whether they fit. The author measured the diameters of the fuse wires on a standard card with 5-amp, 15-amp and 30-amp wires on it. A micrometer screw gauge was used to make the measurements, and the results are shown below:

I (amps)	d (mm)	$I \div d^{\frac{3}{2}}$	$I \div d^{\frac{5}{4}}$
30	0.860	37.6	36.2
15	0.500	42.4	35.7
5	0.205	53.9	36.2

Since I increases with d, we know that m must be greater than 0 (if it can be found at all). Sticking to powers which can be found using a simple calculator with a square root key, we can test $m = 1, \frac{3}{2}, \frac{5}{4}$, etc. The table shows that for our three results the current rating of the wire varies very closely as the $\frac{5}{4}$ power of its diameter, and we expect this to hold for fuse wires of any given material.

3.13. Ramps and radios: Pythagoras

One of the best-known results in the whole of mathematics is the theorem of Pythagoras. It is known by many people with no great claim to be mathematicians (Mr Danny Kaye and the Cowardly Lion from *The Wizard of Oz*, to name but two). It tells us that the lengths of the hypotenuse, perpendicular and base of a right-angled triangle (shown below) are

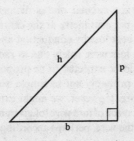

related by the equation

$$h^2 = p^2 + b^2.$$

The result holds for a triangle in a plane. There is also a three-dimensional form of it: if we travel a distance e east, then n north, then distance v vertically, our distance l from the starting point is given by

$$l^2 = e^2 + n^2 + v^2.$$

(Of course, we must not make e, n and v too large, or the curvature of the earth will make the equation slightly in error.) Pythagoras's theorem, then, involves *sums of squares*, which occur quite often in mathematics – we shall later see their use in statistics (section 3.14). Some calculators have a special $[\![M + x^2]\!]$ key which squares the display number and adds it into the memory. On a calculator with memory and automatic K constant we can work out $(a^2 + b^2)^{\frac{1}{2}}$ as follows (taking $a = 1.20$, $b = 2.714$ as an example):

$$[\![1.2 \times = MS\ 2.714 \times = + MR = \sqrt{}]\!]\quad \boxed{2.9674561}.$$

On some calculators the $[\![=]\!]$ stroke before $[\![\sqrt{}]\!]$ is not necessary, but we included it for safety, since some calculators with A.O.S. logic would work out

$$b^2 + \sqrt{a^2} = b^2 + a$$

if the $[\![=]\!]$ stroke (which completes the calculation of $b^2 + a^2$) were omitted.

Suppose that we want to use a ramp to roll some barrels up on to the back of a truck which is 6 ft high, and we have them on a platform which is 3 ft high. If the ramp is 6 ft long, but there is only a space of 2 ft for the end of the ramp on the platform, how far from the edge of the platform must the lorry stop? The situation can be described using the diagram:

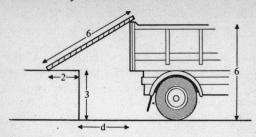

The right-angled triangle which interests us has a base of length $d+2$, a perpendicular of length 3 ($=6-3$), and a hypotenuse of length 6. We thus have

$$6^2 = 3^2 + (d+2)^2.$$

Working the numbers out gives $(d+2)^2 = 27$, so that $d = 3.2$ ft approximately, since $\sqrt{27} = 5.196152$ to six places.

Readers who are interested in radio may have encountered the use of the Pythagoras theorem in connection with the theory of tuning circuits. If an ordinary resistance of R ohms, an inductance (i.e., a coil) of L henries and a capacitor of C farads are connected in series, the combination will not pass direct current if a battery is connected across the circuit, because the gap between the capacitor plates breaks the circuit:

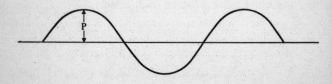

However, an alternating current generator of frequency f cycles per second *will* drive a current round the circuit (an alternating current, of course). An alternating voltage or current looks like this when shown on a graph:

It is usual to give as the 'size' of an alternating voltage or current the peak value P. If by V_0 and I_0 we mean the peak voltage and current, respectively, for our simple LCR circuit, the law which relates V_0 to I_0 is given by

$$V_0 = I_0 \times |Z|.$$

$|Z|$ (the modulus of the impedance) plays a role similar to that of the resistance in an ordinary direct-current circuit. One of the interesting results of the theory of tuning circuits is that $|Z|$ can be calculated from a simple geometrical calculation, which is shown by the diagram below ($|Z|$ is the length of Z):

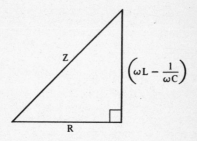

The number ω is the angular frequency, given by the formula $\omega = 2\pi f$. Using the Pythagoras theorem, then, $|Z|$ can be calculated for any frequency f, and it is clear that for a given V we get the biggest current I when $|Z|$ is at its smallest. This will happen when the perpendicular has zero length, which happens at a frequency f given by

$$\omega \times L = \frac{1}{\omega C}$$

i.e., $$f = \frac{1}{2\pi\sqrt{LC}}.$$

This is the resonance frequency of the tuned circuit; the signal from a radio antenna will contain a mixture of the frequencies from various transmitters, but the circuit will 'stop' frequencies other than f by presenting a higher resistance to them.

3.14. Kinds of average

The word 'average' is used in everyday language, but in mathematical terminology it is ambiguous, since several different kinds of average can be defined, each being useful for particular kinds of calculation. We will list three types of average below, and then indicate where we have encountered them in this book. For n numbers the averages are defined by:

Arithmetic mean : $A = \dfrac{1}{n} \times$ (sum of the n numbers)

Geometric mean : $G =$ (product of the n numbers)$^{\frac{1}{n}}$

Harmonic mean : $H =$ (arithmetic means of the n reciprocals)$^{-1}$

The arithmetic mean is the number which most people mean when they speak loosely of the average of a set of numbers. However, we saw in section 2.10 that calculation of an arithmetic mean of the speeds over two halves of a journey gives an incorrect average speed; it is the harmonic mean of the speeds which must be used. The theory of resistances in parallel (section 3.12) and of the image distance for a lens (section 3.11) can also be worded so as to involve harmonic means. Thus: the resistance produced by two parallel resistors is equal to half the harmonic mean of the two resistances; the harmonic mean of the image and object distances for a thin lens is equal to a constant. The geometric mean of two numbers appeared in section 2.4 as the length of side of a square which has an area equal to that of a given rectangle. In general the arithmetic mean A of a set of numbers is always bigger than the geometric mean G of the numbers, but if the numbers are close together then A and G are almost identical. (We note here that all three types of average obey the 'common-sense' principle that the average of n equal numbers, all equal to x, is just x. For example, if we work out A, G or H for the three numbers 3.12, 3.12 and 3.12, they all work out to 3.12.) To see how A and G are related we can use an example from section 2.6, concerning the average mortgage interest rate for a year. We have a rate of 10% for 3 months and a rate of 11% for 9 months. The multiplying factors for a year which go with the two interest rates are 1.10 and 1.11, and the arithmetic mean of three 1.10s and nine 1.11s is

$$A = [(9 \times 1.11) + (3 \times 1.10)] \div 12 = 1.1075.$$

Key strokes: $[\![3 \ \times \ 1.11 \ + \ 1.1 \ \times \ 3 \ \div \ 12 \ =]\!]$.

(Why do these key strokes work? Write it out and see!)

The factor 1.1075 corresponds to an interest rate of 10.75%, which we found in section 2.6 by taking an arithmetic mean *of the percentages themselves*. This gives the same answer, because adding 1 to all twelve numbers simply adds 1 to the arithmetic mean. This simple additive property is *not* true for the geometric and harmonic means: for instance, adding 10 m.p.h. to the speed over each half of a journey does not add 10 m.p.h. to the average speed for the whole journey. Now, for the mortgage problem, if we think in terms of compound interest (section 2.5) we regard the multiplying factors as the numbers to concentrate on. Replacing the product of multiplying factor $(1.10)^3 \times (1.11)^9$ by some equivalent factor $(G)^{12}$ is then accomplished by using a geometric mean:

$$G = [(1.1)^3 \times (1.11)^9]^{\frac{1}{12}}.$$

To get a twelfth root on an ordinary calculator is usually a little lengthy; we can use our knowledge of the law of indices here, however, to write G in the form

$$G = [(1.1) \times (1.11)^3]^{\frac{1}{4}}$$

and so can use the following key strokes on a calculator with automatic K constant:

$$[\![1.1 \ \times \ 1.11 \ = \ = \ = \ \sqrt{} \ \sqrt{}\,]\!] \quad \boxed{1.1074915}.$$

The resulting average interest rate is thus 10.7491%, which differs from our previous (arithmetic mean) result by 1 part in 12,000.

A fourth kind of average which appears in statistical work and in various scientific theories is the root mean square average R, which is defined for n numbers by

$$R = (\text{arithmetic mean of the } n \text{ squares})^{\frac{1}{2}}.$$

Suppose that we keep on repeatedly measuring something, or keep on repeating some experiment to determine some quantity. We could imagine our results set out in a table:

	Result	Deviation, d	d^2
	153.2	−0.33	0.1089
	157.1	3.57	12.7449
	151.5	−2.03	4.1209
	154.2	0.67	0.4489
	152.1	−1.43	2.0449
	149.9	−3.63	13.1769
	153.8	0.27	0.0729
	154.7	1.17	1.3669
	152.8	−0.73	0.5329
	156.0	2.47	6.1009
Sum	1535.30	0.00	40.7210
Divide by 10	153.53		4.0721

The quantity $\frac{1}{10} \times$ (sum of numbers) at the bottom of the left column is the arithmetic mean A of the ten numbers. The deviation d (second column) is the difference between each reading and A. The last row of the third column contains the arithmetic mean of the ten d^2 values. Taking its square root gives us the root mean square average σ of the deviations, i.e., 2.018. In scientific work it is quite common to present a short summary of the above kind of calculation by quoting A and σ, e.g., by saying in this case that the quantity which we were trying to find by our repeated measurements has a value of 153.5 ± 2.0. This is $A \pm \sigma$, with the values of A and σ rounded appropriately because the original data was quoted to only one decimal place. Although two of the results differed from the mean by more than 3, most of the results are closer to the mean, and this makes us confident that the 'minority report' of the two points is too pessimistic. The use of σ as the error estimate allows roughly for this kind of judgement about the relative weighting which is to be assigned to the various results. In statistics the root mean square average of the deviations is called the *standard deviation* of the results, and under certain circumstances definite statements can be made about the small probability that the true result could be outside the range $A \pm \sigma$.

While the tabular layout given above helps to explain the calculation of a standard deviation, we should note that it is *not* necessary to work out the numbers in the d and d^2 columns in order to get the standard deviation. The value of σ for a table of n numbers can be worked out using the equivalent equations:

$$\sigma^2 = (\text{sum of squares} \div n) - A^2$$

$$\text{Sum of squares} = n(A^2 + \sigma^2).$$

The second equation is simply the first one in a re-arranged form, and may be interpreted as follows. If all of the n numbers are equal they must equal A, which yields nA^2 for the sum of squares. The extra term $n\sigma^2$ is then a correction term which allows for the fact that the numbers actually spread over an 'average' range σ around A. The whole calculation can be done using only the first column numbers and their squares. It can be made even shorter, however, if we subtract 140 from all the numbers in our specimen table of results. This merely subtracts 140 from A, as we noted previously, but gives smaller numbers to be used in the calculation. At the same time it *leaves σ unchanged*, so we simply proceed as though the numbers in the first column were 13.2, 17.1, etc., and right at the end add back the 140 (to A only) to get the final result $A \pm \sigma$.

The arithmetic mean A has two interesting properties which are relevant to our calculation above. First, the sum of the deviations d from A is zero (see the sum at the foot of the second column). Second, the sum of the squared differences, i.e., $(x_1 - \alpha)^2 + (x_2 - \alpha)^2 + \ldots$ for the n numbers $x_1, x_2, \ldots x_n$ is smallest when the fixed number α is equal to A, the arithmetic mean of the n numbers. This means that the smallest possible value which this sum of squared differences can take is equal to σ^2, the square of the standard deviation as we have defined it. Our definition involves the 'standard' choice $\alpha = A$.

We mention briefly here two examples of the use of the R.M.S. average in simple science. The kinetic theory of gases says that the atoms of a gas move about at high speeds, but not all at the same speed. The guiding principle is that if we have a large number n of identical atoms, such as hydrogen atoms, the *arithmetic* mean of their kinetic energies is proportional to the absolute temperature of the gas. (Absolute temperature = 273 + Centigrade temperature.) The *kinetic energy* of an atom is given by the formula $\frac{1}{2}mV^2$, where m is its mass and V is its speed; in order to get the total kinetic energy of the gas we must multiply n by the (arithmetic) mean kinetic energy per atom. If we write this average in the form $\frac{1}{2}mV^2$, then V (called the R.M.S. speed) is a root mean square average of the *speeds* of the atoms. It is usually this R.M.S. speed which is meant when reference is made to 'the' speed of the atoms in a gas (for example, V is around 45 km per sec for the molecules in air).

In section 3.12 we noted that an electric current of I amps passing through a resistance of R ohms produces heat at a rate H given by $H = I^2R$. At first sight it appears that H is proportional to R, but this is *only* true if I is held constant. In fact, if a generator or battery of voltage V is connected across the resistor then Ohm's law says that $V = IR$. This gives the result

$$H = RI^2 = R(V \div R)^2$$
$$= V^2 \div R$$

and shows that H is actually *inversely* proportional to R under those circumstances. However, if the generator supplies *alternating* current then the voltage V across the resistance varies at so many cycles per second, swinging between zero and some peak voltage V_0. If we work out H by using $V_0^2 \div R$ we get too large an answer, since for most of the time the voltage is less than V_0. There will be an 'average' voltage, the R.M.S. voltage, which must be used in the formula to give the correct rate of heat production H. For a simple alternating current generator this R.M.S. voltage is given by

Peak voltage = $\sqrt{2} \times$ R.M.S. voltage.

The R.M.S. voltage is the number often quoted as 'the' voltage since it would, for example, be the relevant voltage if we were operating an electrical heating coil. The British R.M.S. mains voltage of 230 volts actually corresponds to an instantaneous voltage which goes up to the peak value $230 \times \sqrt{2} = 325$ volts. As our two examples illustrate, the R.M.S. average crops up whenever what matters is the *square* of something (whether speed, voltage or some other variable).

3.15. Sums of products again. Complex numbers

In preceding sections we have worked out numbers such as *the* square root of 2, *the* cube root of 9.23, etc. When we refer to *the* something, we are really assuming that there is *only* one of them or that we are not being ambiguous. Now, if we put -2 into a calculator and square it, we get 4, just as we do when we square $+2$. This shows that both $+2$ and -2 qualify as square roots of 4, and illustrates the rule 'minus times minus equals plus' of arithmetic. Similarly $-1.414...$ and $+1.414...$ are square roots of 2. Thus 4 has *two* square roots at least. What about poor old -4? We cannot find a square root for it, because squaring either a positive or negative number can only give us a positive number. (If you put -4 into a calculator and press the square root key you will get an error indication.) In many branches of mathematics and science it is useful to be democratic and let negative numbers have square roots, which can be done (by force!) by introducing the symbol i to represent 'the square root of minus one'. Most scientists would be somewhat discomfited if asked what i *is*, but they certainly know what it does! It is used in just the same way as an ordinary number, except that i^2 is taken to be -1. For example,

$$(2i)^2 = 2 \times 2 \times i \times i = (2 \times 2) \times (i^2)$$
$$= 4 \times (-1) = -4$$

so 2i is a square root of -4, and so is $-2i$. It turns out that we get two square roots now for every number, whether positive or negative. In the case of cube roots it turns out that every number has three cube roots if we allow i into our arithmetic, and in general, every number has n nth roots. In dealing with such problems we have to use 'mixed' numbers such as $2 + 3i$, which are called *complex numbers*. The ordinary 'old' numbers are then called *real* numbers (e.g., 2 is 'really' shorthand for $2 + 0i$). The numbers i, 2i (multiples of i) are called *imaginary* numbers, and they got this name historically because that is what they are, although nowadays most scientists would say that, because they can be used, they are just as 'real' as real numbers. (This is really a problem for ontology, the branch of philosophy which studies existence, or 'what there is'.)

To multiply together two complex numbers we use the 'sum of products' rule:

$$(a+ib)(c+id) = ac+iad+ibc+i^2bd.$$

To get this far we have used rules such as $aid = iad$ (i.e., we have used commutativity of multiplication). Now, on replacing i^2 by -1, and using commutativity of addition, we get

$$(a+ib)(c+id) = (ac-bd)+i(ad+bc).$$

The way to work out sums of products (such as the two numbers in brackets) on a calculator has been explained in section 3.2. Suppose we look at the cube of a complex number, say $-1+\sqrt{3}i$. We find

$$(-1+i\sqrt{3})^2 = 1-2i\sqrt{3}+3i^2$$
$$= -2-2i\sqrt{3}$$

and

$$(-1+i\sqrt{3})^3 = (-1+i\sqrt{3})(-2-2i\sqrt{3})$$
$$= 2+2i\sqrt{3}-2i\sqrt{3}-6i^2$$
$$= 8.$$

So it seems that $-1+i\sqrt{3}$ is a cube root of 8! Similarly $-1-i\sqrt{3}$ is also a cube root of 8, giving us *three* cube roots for 8, since the real number 2 is also a cube root (indeed, it is the only one we would usually think of). If we use the principle that doubling a number multiplies its cube by eight, we conclude that the numbers 1, $-\frac{1}{2}+\frac{1}{2}i\sqrt{3}$, $-\frac{1}{2}-\frac{1}{2}i\sqrt{3}$, are *cube roots of unity*. In engineering applications of complex numbers the particular symbol ω is sometimes used for $-\frac{1}{2}+\frac{1}{2}i\sqrt{3}$, and $-\frac{1}{2}-\frac{1}{2}i\sqrt{3}$ is then written as ω^2. (Why? see exercise 7.)

3.16. Derivatives. The calculus

In section 3.5. we saw how useful the exponent notation is for treating powers of numbers close to 1, and we exploited this to help with cube root extraction. We can also use it to look at a basic concept of the calculus, the concept of the *derivative* or *differential coefficient* of a function. Suppose that we work out the third powers of two numbers, x and $x+h$, which are very close together (which means that h is very tiny). We find

$$(x+h)^3 = x^3(1+hx^{-1})^3$$

on writing $x+h$ as a product and using the rule $(ab)^3 = a^3b^3$. We know from section 3.5. that we can set (for very small h)

$$x^3(1+hx^{-1})^3 = x^3(1+3hx^{-1})$$
$$= x^3+3hx^2.$$

This shows that if we increase x by the amount h then the value of x^3 increases by h times $3x^2$. The coefficient $3x^2$ which multiplies h to give the change in x^3 is called the *differential coefficient* or *derivative* of x^3. By using a similar argument we can see that the derivative of x^2 is $2x$, and so on, and the rule is that x^n has derivative nx^{n-1}. To find the derivative of a function numerically on a calculator (if we do not know a formula for the derivative) we can work out the function at x and at $x+h$ and divide the difference by h. For example, for x^3, we can start at $x = 2$ and use $h = 10^{-1}$, 10^{-2} and so on. Our estimates of the derivative are then

12.61, 12.0601, 12.006, 12, 12, 12,

indicating that 12 is the derivative. ($3x^2 = 12$ if $x = 2$.)

To get the derivative of a polynomial (as studied in section 2.6) we simply add together the derivatives for the individual terms. For example, the polynomial

$$x^3-2x^2+x-1$$

has the derivative

$$3x^2-4x+1$$

(the constant -1 has zero derivative, since it does not change if we change x a little). If we work out the value of x^3-2x^2+x-1 for many x values we can draw a graph to display the results, using the symbol y for x^3-2x^2+x-1:

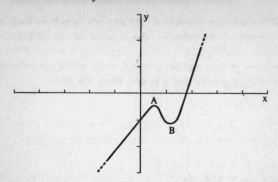

We see that the curve has two points at which it 'bends back', a maximum at A and a minimum at B. At such a point we can see by eye that the curve is horizontal, so that increasing x by a very tiny amount h causes no change in the value of $x^3 - 2x^2 + x - 1$. But this change is given by $(3x^2 - 4x + 1)h$ according to our algebra. It must be the case that

$$3x^2 - 4x - 1 = 0$$

at A and B. This equation is a quadratic equation, and many readers will know that there is a standard formula to obtain its two roots. What we see here is that the roots of the quadratic equation are the x values at which the function $x^3 - 2x^2 + x - 1$ has a 'turning point'. There is an important branch of mathematics, the *variational calculus*, which uses this kind of approach, namely showing that the roots of some equation are the x values at which some function has a turning point; this trick is often useful in theoretical physics. For our simple example we can work out the function at intervals of 0.01 between 0.3 and 0.4 to get

$-0.853, \ -0.852409, \ -0.852032, \ -0.851863, \ -0.851896$, etc.

At $x = 0.33$ we seem to have a maximum, which we can locate more closely by using smaller x intervals. The exact answer, $\frac{1}{3}$, is a repeating decimal, $0.333\ldots$ Similarly we can find a minimum at $x = 1$. If we require the value of $x^3 - 2x^2 + x - 1$ at the maximum, we have it to three figures, -0.852, even using an x value which is wrong by 0.02. It is this insensitivity of certain results to the 'input' which is exploited in the variational calculus. The numbers worked out on the calculator tell us that the turning point at $x = \frac{1}{3}$ is a maximum. To the left of $x = \frac{1}{3}$ the derivative is positive, at $x = \frac{1}{3}$ it is zero, and to the right of $x = \frac{1}{3}$ it is negative. Thus, at a *maximum* the derivative is *decreasing*. To check whether the derivative $3x^2 - 4x + 1$ is increasing or decreasing we can work out its *own* derivative! This is $6x - 4$, by our rule. At $x = \frac{1}{3}$, this equals -2, but at $x = 1$ it equals 2. This shows that the turning points at $\frac{1}{3}$ and 1 are, respectively, a maximum and a minimum. The function $6x - 4$ is called the *second derivative* of the function $x^3 - 2x^2 + x - 1$, and third and higher derivatives can be produced by continuing the process. The third derivative here is 6 (a constant), so the fourth derivative is zero.

3.17. The slaves problem (a diversion)

In section 3.15, dealing with square roots, we noted that the product of two negative numbers is positive. (Try some examples on a calculator.) Also, a positive number times a negative number gives a negative number. For example,

$$1 \times 1 = 1; \quad (-1) \times (-1) = 1; \quad 1 \times (-1) = -1.$$

There are several simple mathematical systems which have similar properties; even and odd integers, for example. If E denotes even and O odd we have the addition rules

$$E + E = E; \quad O + O = E; \quad E + O = O.$$

The first equation means (for example) that the sum of two even numbers is always an even number. The two systems exhibited above show an *isomorphism* (sameness of form), that is, they are the same if viewed in a sufficiently abstract manner, without worrying about the meaning of the symbols $+$, $\times$, E, 1, etc. The study of isomorphisms between mathematical structures is one of the important aims of modern abstract algebra.

Now, here is the problem, as told to the author in his undergraduate days. The wicked Sultan puts his prisoner in a room, with two guards, who can only say 'Yes' or 'No' in response to a question. The room has two doors, A and B, one leading to freedom, the other to execution. One slave always tells the truth, the other one always lies. What question should the prisoner ask? Dr Johnson observed that it concentrates a man's mind wonderfully if he is about to be hanged, but we may well wonder whether our hypothetical prisoner would be in a fit state to think logically! If he were, he could reason as follows: 'If I have two numbers, one being 1, the other -1, I definitely know that their product is -1. If I ask either slave the question "Would that other slave say that door A is the door to freedom?" I *must* get the opposite of the truth, and so find out whether door A or door B is the one I require.' The abstract structure of the two-slave system is the same as that of the two mathematical systems displayed in the preceding paragraph. The preceding reasoning was that used by the author when he first heard the problem, and seemed quite natural to someone who had read about symbolic logic and the use of binary numbers such as 0 and 1 to represent truth values. At the time, however, his colleagues were inclined to the belief that 'nobody's mind works like that', and openly charged him with having heard the answer before!

3.18. Comments on the exercises

This chapter has included quite a lot of material, although if you look through it carefully you will see that in the main it has proceeded by making variations on one or two simple themes. The procedure of making fruitful new combinations of a few simple 'old' ideas is common to creative work in most of the sciences, and it should be one of the aims of teaching to encourage the pupil to develop the flexibility of mind which makes this creativity possible. In most scientific work, the initial creative impulse must be followed by a period of careful analytical testing. A study of the biographies of mathematicians and scientists shows that very few people, even of the highest ability, possess the creative and the analytic abilities to the same degree. Indeed, even in one person the relative strengths of the two powers vary with experience and age.

There are quite a lot of exercises given below, since an enormous amount of mathematics can be developed from the 'clues' which we have given in this chapter. Once again, we suggest that the reader should read through the exercises, even if not wishing to work them all out.

Exercises

1. Work out $\left(\dfrac{a^2}{d}+d\right)d$ with $a = 1$, $d = 0.00001$ and then with a and d reversed. Both results should equal a^2+d^2, according to the discussion of section 3.2. Do they?

Solution

The results are 1.00 in both cases, whereas a^2+d^2 equals $1 + 10^{-10}$. 10^{-10} is too small to show on an eight-figure calculator. In general, expressions which are equal in theory may not give exactly equal results on a calculator because of rounding errors.

2. Readers acquainted with the material of section 3.12 will remember that the effective resistance R (in ohms) which results when two resistances of a ohms and b ohms are connected in parallel is given by an equation involving reciprocals:

$$\frac{1}{R} = \frac{1}{a}+\frac{1}{b}.$$

Can you work out R, knowing a and b, without using your calculator's memory, or a note-pad to write down a^{-1}?

Solution

Multiplying by ab gives

$$\frac{ab}{R} = a+b$$

$$R = \frac{ab}{(a+b)} = (a+b)^{-1}ab.$$

The key strokes on an automatic K constant machine are

$$[\![a \ + \ b \ \div \ = \ = \ \times \ a \ \times \ b \ =]\!].$$

3. If your calculator can work out square roots and squares, try the following sequence of operations: Enter 2; take square root; square result; take square root; square result; and so on. Probably what you will get at successive squarings is a number which gradually decreases. Why?

Solution

Many calculators simply chop off the end of a number to display it, so that at each step they *reduce* the answer a little, if it is a positive number. A few calculators round scientifically, showing 0.1231325|821 as 0.1231326, etc. 'Chopping off' would give 0.1231325.

4. In section 3.4 we saw that to get square and cube roots of a number y in our iterative process we had to use the formulae

$$\frac{1}{2}\frac{y}{x}+\frac{1}{2}x$$
$$\frac{1}{3}\frac{y}{x^2}+\frac{2}{3}x.$$

Can you guess what the formula will be for the fifth root of x? Can you prove it? Check it on your calculator by evaluating $(5)^{\frac{1}{5}}$. Also work out $(5)^{\frac{1}{5}}$ by the quick method of section 3.5 if you have a square root key on your calculator.

Solution

$$\frac{1}{5}\frac{y}{x^4}+\frac{4}{5}x.$$

Using $x = \sqrt[5]{y}+h$, and the result that $(1+z)^{-4} = 1-4z$ for small z, we can proceed as in the text to show that the h terms vanish. We find $(5)^{\frac{1}{5}} = 1.3797296$. Using ten square roots, the short method gives $(5)^{\frac{1}{5}} = 1.3798$ to four places.

5. We saw in section 3.2 how to work out a sum of two products. Can you construct a way of working out a sum of squares, i.e.

$$(a^2+b^2+c^2)$$

on a calculator without a memory?

Solution

Use $a^2 \div b + b \times b \div c + c \times c$.

6. Try the 'stretching' process of section 3.6 again for $\sqrt{2}$, but start from the first estimate 1.413 instead of 1.414. What difference does this make to the result?

Solution

$(1.413)^2 = 1.996569 = 2 - 0.003431$.

Thus, if $\sqrt{2} = 1.413 + h$, we find

$$h = \frac{0.003431}{2.826 + h}.$$

This leads to $h = 0.0012135623$, after three steps of iteration. Adding 1.413 gives $\sqrt{2} = 1.4142135623$, which has one figure less than the result obtained starting from 1.414.

7. Show that the notation 1, ω, ω^2 for the cube roots of unity (section 3.15) is a sensible one, by showing that one of the three roots is the square of one of the others. If $x^3 = 1$, what does x^4 equal?

Solution

Squaring $-\frac{1}{2} + \frac{1}{2}i\sqrt{3}$, which we call ω, gives $-\frac{1}{2} - \frac{1}{2}i\sqrt{3}$, which we can call ω^2. $x^4 = (1)x = x$, i.e., $x^4 = x$. In particular, then, $\omega^4 = \omega$ if ω is a cube root of unity.

8. An important idea used at several points in this chapter is that of 'getting at the answer indirectly', which we can intuitively represent by the diagram

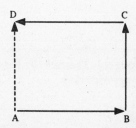

We cannot get directly from A to D, so we go round by $ABCD$. How many arguments in the chapter can you find which show this abstract pattern? This method of transformations is used widely in science (i.e., we transform a problem into some equivalent problem which we can handle).

9. If an object is held at rest and then released so that it falls a distance x in time t, the formula which relates x to t is

$$x = \tfrac{1}{2}gt^2$$

(if we neglect the effects of air resistance). g is a constant, about 981 if t is measured in seconds and x in centimetres. Find the first and second derivatives of x (as t varies), and say what the usual names are which we give to these quantities. Note that we have 'changed the names' in this problem: in the text x was the symbol used in the polynomial. The abstract processes involved do not depend on the names used, of course, and it is the understanding of this basic fact which must be acquired by any beginner when dealing with any kind of mathematical formalism.

Solution

The first derivative is called the speed of the object, and equals gt here. The second derivative is called the acceleration of the object, and equals g here. g is the acceleration due to gravity in this particular problem.

10. Cube the numbers 1.1, 1.01, 1.001, etc., and use the results to set up a table showing how the error $E(x)$ depends on x in the equation

$$(1+x)^{\frac{1}{3}} = 1 + \tfrac{1}{3}x - E(x).$$

Show that as x becomes smaller $E(x)$ becomes closely equal to kx^2, and estimate the constant k. Theoretically k should equal $\tfrac{1}{9}$. Show that the improved approximation

$$(1+x)^{\frac{1}{3}} = 1 + \frac{1}{3}x - \frac{1}{9}x^2$$

can be expressed as

$$\frac{1}{36}[45-(2x-3)^2].$$

Can you work this out without using the calculator's memory?

Solution

Cubing 1.1 gives $(1.1)^3 = 1.331$. Now, we must set $x = 0.331$, i.e., $1+x = 1.331$. Thus, $(1.331)^{\frac{1}{3}} = 1.1 = 1+\frac{1}{3}(0.331)-E(x)$. Thus, at $x = 0.331$, $E = \frac{1}{3}(0.331)-0.1 = 0.01033$.

Calculating similarly for 1.01 and 1.001, and dividing the E values by x^2 in each case gives the following estimates for k:

0.0943, 0.1093, 0.1109, 0.

The zero arises because of rounding errors; $E(x)$ is so small that the calculator cannot display it.

To calculate $\frac{1}{36}[45-(2x-3)^2]$ we cannot use the 45 first if we have no memory. Instead we work out

$$(2x-3)^2-45\div 36$$

and use the $[\![\pm]\!]$ key to change the sign (or just do it mentally).

11. Below we show the stopping distance l (in feet) for a car travelling at a speed v (in miles per hour), as taken from the British Highway Code.

v	30	40	50	60	70
l	75	120	175	240	315

Show that the figures obey the law

$$l = v+\frac{1}{20}v^2.$$

Write this so that it can be worked out using only one entry of v on a calculator. What is the value of l if v is 55 m.p.h.? The first term v in the formula represents the 'thinking-time distance', while $\frac{1}{20}v^2$ is the actual braking distance. What is the thinking time assumed in the tables?

Solution

$$l = \frac{1}{20}[(v+10)^2 - 100]$$

$l = 206.25$ ft at $v = 55$ m.p.h.

v miles per hour is $v \times 1760 \times 3$ feet per hour, which corresponds to $(v \times 1760 \times 3)/3600$ feet per second. (Thus 60 m.p.h. is also 88 feet per second.) At 60 m.p.h., then, 60 feet is covered in $(60 \div 88)$, i.e. 0.682 sec, to three places.

12. In *The History of Western Philosophy*, Bertrand Russell describes the following rule, known to the Greeks, for finding approximations to $\sqrt{2}$. Form two columns, one with elements $a_0, a_1, a_2, \ldots$, the other with elements $b_0, b_1, b_2, \ldots$ Each a is the sum of the preceding a and the preceding b. Each b is the sum of the preceding b and twice the preceding a. a_0 and b_0 are both 1. The ratios (b_n/a_n) get nearer to $\sqrt{2}$ as n increases. Try this on a calculator and see if you can find the law which relates the successive approximations to $\sqrt{2}$.

Solution

1, 1.5, 1.4, 1.4166, 1.4137931, 1.4142857, 1.4142011 etc.

Use the symbol f_n for (b_n/a_n). We have the law

$$a_{n+1} = a_n + b_n = a_n + f_n a_n$$
$$b_{n+1} = 2a_n + b_n = 2a_n + f_n a_n$$

so that

$$f_{n+1} = \frac{b_{n+1}}{a_{n+1}} = \frac{(2 + f_n)}{(1 + f_n)}$$
$$= 1 + (1 + f_n)^{-1}.$$

This works easily as an iterative process if we have a reciprocal key, although it is not as good as the process described in section 3.4. To find $\sqrt{x}$ instead of $\sqrt{2}$, the rule is

$$f_{n+1} = 1 + (x - 1)(1 + f_n)^{-1}.$$

For a calculator with a memory and a reciprocal key, we can keep $x - 1$ in the memory and perform the successive steps easily. The process of section 3.4, although taking fewer cycles, does require the entry of x at each cycle.

13. If the current rating I (in amps) of a fuse wire is related to its diameter (in millimetres) by the relation $I = 36d^{\frac{5}{4}}$, as in section 3.12, find the d value needed to give a 20-amp fuse.

Solution

Using a few simple d values we can work out their associated I values:

d	0.80	0.70	0.60
I	27.23	23.05	19.01.

To work out, for example, the I value for $d = 0.80$, we use the key strokes $[\![0.80 \times = = = = \sqrt{} \sqrt{} \times 36 =]\!]$ (with automatic K constant).

The three results indicate that the relationship between I and d is almost linear: I changes by 4.04 and then by 4.18 as d makes two successive changes of 0.10. To get $I = 20$ we must move almost exactly one quarter of the way from 19.01 to 23.05, and can estimate d by moving one quarter of the way from 0.60 to 0.70. (We are using what is usually called *linear interpolation* here.) This suggests the value $d = 0.625$; putting this in the formula gives $I = 20.00$, so the S.I.A.S. method shows the validity of the result.

14. Consider two thin lenses which are 10 cm apart, one lens having a focal length of 5 cm and the other a focal length of 4 cm. Calculate the way in which the pair of lenses behaves by treating them one at a time, as follows. Start with an object at distance u_1 to the left of one lens. Calculate the image distance v_1 from the thin lens formula. Then use $10 - v_1$ as the object distance u_2 for the *second* lens and find the image distance v_2. Find the v_2 value for $u_1 = \infty$, and call it V_2. Find the u_1 value for $v_2 = \infty$ and call it U_1. Show that as u_1 varies the product $(u_1 - U_1)(v_2 - V_2)$ remains equal to a constant K.

Solution

$u_1 = \infty$ gives $v_1 = 5$, so that $u_2 = 10 - 5 = 5$.

This gives $V_2 = 20$ cm.

$v_2 = \alpha$ gives $u_2 = 4$, so that $v_1 = 10 - 4 = 6$.

This gives $U_1 = 30$ cm.

For a variety of numerical u_1 values we find $(u_1 - 30)(v_2 - 20) = 400$.

The *algebraic* solution of the problem gives, for lenses with focal lengths f_1 and f_2 and separation d, the following results (with $l = f_1 + f_2 - d$):

$$V_2 = \frac{f_2}{l}(f_1 - d)$$

$$U_1 = \frac{f_1}{l}(f_2 - d)$$

$$K = \left(\frac{f_1 f_2}{l}\right)^2.$$

15. Consider two numbers x and y. Show that their harmonic, geometric and arithmetic means (section 3.14) obey the relation

$$H \leqslant G \leqslant A \ (\leqslant \text{ means 'is less than or equal to')}.$$

Solution

If the arithmetic mean is A, and if x is greater than A by an amount h, then y must be *smaller* than A by an amount h. We thus have the result

$$xy = (A + h)(A - h)$$
$$= A^2 - h^2.$$

Thus we must have $xy \leqslant A^2$, and since G^2 equals xy, it follows that $G \leqslant A$. The harmonic mean H is given by

$$H = (2xy) \div (x + y).$$

This can be written in terms of G and A:

$$H = (2G^2) \div (2A)$$
$$= \frac{G^2}{A} = \frac{G}{A} \times G.$$

Since $G \leqslant A$, it follows that the factor $G \div A$ is less than or equal to 1, and so that $H \leqslant G$.

16. Given a meter which measures currents up to 0.1 amp and has a resistance of 10.0 ohms, what could we do to make it measure currents up to 1.0 amp? (See section 3.12.)

Solution

We put a resistance (the shunt resistance) across the meter, so that when 1.0 amp flows through the circuit only 0.1 amp goes through the meter. The other 0.9 amp goes through the shunt. This means that we have two resistances in parallel; since I is inversely proportional to R, if we want the ratio of currents to be 9:1, the ratio of *resistance* must be 1:9. The meter resistance is 10.0 ohms, so we must use a shunt resistance of $10.0 \div 9 = 1.11$ ohms.

17. Given three resistors, each of 1.0 ohm, what different resistance values can we make using series and parallel combinations?

Solution

3 in series: $R = 3$
3 in parallel: $R = \frac{1}{3}$
(2 in series) in parallel with 1: $R = \frac{2}{3}$
(2 in parallel) in series with 1: $R = \frac{3}{2}$

18. Two unknown resistances r and R in series give a total resistance of 10 ohms. Show that we could not get a resistance of more than 2.5 ohms by connecting them in parallel.

Solution

$S = r + R = 10$
$P = (r \times R) \div (r + R)$
$\quad = r \times (10 - r) \div 10$.

Working out P for $r = 0$, 1, 2 etc. we quickly see that it has its greatest value $P = 2.5$ at $r = 5$; in general the maximum P value appears at $r = \frac{1}{2}S$ and has the value $P = \frac{1}{4}S$. Note that for our example any r value between 2.8 and 7.2 yields a P value between 2.0 and 2.5. The mathematics of this calculation can be given another interpretation: it shows that if we draw a family of rectangles, all with the same perimeter, the one with the largest area is the square one (with both sides of equal length). If, on the other hand, we consider rectangles of fixed *area*, the square is the one with the smallest perimeter. If we are allowed to have *any* shape enclosing the fixed area, a circle gives the smallest perimeter. (For example, to get 1 square centimetre takes a square of perimeter 4 cm and a circle of perimeter about 3.5 cm.)

19. According to the formula of section 3.12 the resistance of a piece of wire of length l and cross-sectional area a is proportional to $l \div a$. Consider the following 'thought experiment': imagine the wire to be made up of two adjoining 'half wires', that is, think of it as having an imaginary cut, as shown:

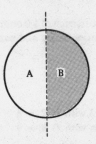

Thinking of the A and B 'wires' as though they are two resistances in parallel, work out their combined resistance and show that it correctly equals the resistance of the full wire.

Solution

Each portion, A and B, has half the cross-sectional area of the full wire, and thus twice the resistance. However, connecting two resistances of size $2W$ in parallel gives a total resistance of W, so that our result is consistent. What it really shows is the correctness of supposing that resistance is inversely proportional to area; the reader may like to try showing that the calculation works equally well if we split the wire into two *unequal* parts. Astute readers may object that the calculation is not correct, because A and B *are* really connected all the time; however, the current flows *along* the wire, so there is no 'cross-current' linking our imaginary A and B halves.

20. What is the resistance of this circuit, made up of 1, 2 and 3 ohm resistors?

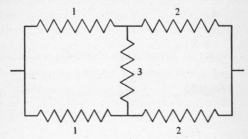

Solution

By symmetry it is clear that the voltages at the opposite ends of the 3-ohm resistor must be the same. Thus no current flows through that resistor, which means that it has no effect. The battery driving the circuit thus 'sees' only two equal 3-ohm resistances in parallel, giving a total resistance of 1.5 ohms.

21. The equation used to find cube roots from square roots in section 2.13 is

$$\frac{1}{3} = \frac{1}{4} \times \left(1 + \frac{1}{3}\right).$$

Devise a formula which starts with $\frac{1}{16}$ on the right, and use it to find $(1.327)^{\frac{1}{3}}$.

Devise a formula for the fifth root of a number, and test it for $2^{\frac{1}{5}}$.

Solution

$$\frac{1}{3} = \frac{1}{16} \times \left(5 + \frac{1}{3}\right).$$

To use this equation we put $(1.327)^5$ in the memory; starting with the first guess 1.1 we use the key strokes

$[\![1.1 \; \times \; \mathbf{M\,R} \; = \; \sqrt{} \; \sqrt{} \; \sqrt{} \; \sqrt{} \; \times \; \mathbf{M\,R}]\!]$ etc.

The results are 1.1, 1.0989658, 1.0989012, 1.0988971, 1.0988969, which are (except for rounding errors) the same results as obtained at every second stage of the process described in section 2.13. The formula to be used for the fifth root is

$$\frac{1}{5} = \frac{1}{16} \times \left(3 + \frac{1}{5} \right).$$

The process based on this gives as a typical sequence of estimates for $2^{\frac{1}{5}}$ the numbers 1, 1.1387885, 1.1480764, 1.1486594, 1.1486958, 1.1486981, 1.1486983.

Chapter 4
Scientific Calculators and Calculations

4.1. General introduction

In a study of trigonometry quantities such as the cosine and sine of an angle may be required, while in elementary physics the exponential function and the natural logarithm often appear. A *scientific calculator* is one which has special keys to give the value of $\cos x$, $\sin x$, $\exp x$, $\ln x$, etc., for our input x value. Many scientific calculators also have a key marked $[\![x^y]\!]$, which will work out the yth power of a number x. Although such a key in principle makes a square root key redundant, many machines do keep a $[\![\sqrt{}]\!]$ key as well, since the square root is so often needed. Scientific calculators use the scientific method of displaying numbers (e.g., $3517 = 3.517 \times 10^3$), as described in section 1.6. To enter the number 3517 it is usually possible to directly put in 3517 *or* to put in $[\![3.517 \; EE \; 3]\!]$, using the 'enter exponent' key to indicate that what follows is the exponent. For a very large or very small number, of course, the direct entry is impossible, so the $[\![EE]\!]$ key must be used. We can use various entry patterns to get the same number; thus $[\![35.17 \; EE \; 2]\!]$ still gives us the number 3517, displayed as 35.17×10^2. However, on most machines pressing the $[\![=]\!]$ key then gives the display in the 'standard' form 3.517×10^3.

The aim of this chapter is three-fold. First, to explain the meaning of the various scientific functions, starting from the simple ideas of the earlier chapters. Second, to show a few uses of scientific calculators in some scientific problems. Third (the most creative part), to show how an understanding of the scientific functions enables us to devise ways of working them out on a simple calculator! This last step is probably the tour-de-force of the book, and shows clearly the union of theory and practice which was referred to in the introduction. The question may be asked (indeed, has been asked), 'Why bother to ape a scientific calculator with a simple one?' Well, in the first place, we learn more deeply about the mathematics involved, which is part of the aim of this book. Also, the methods *work*, and quickly too, so that we can actually *do* the calculations without owning a fully-fledged scientific calculator, though it may be agreed that a serious university student *should* invest some extra money on one. Nevertheless, learning to think is both worthwhile and also fun!

4.2. Trigonometric functions

For readers who are a bit hazy about trigonometry we can start by looking at the triangle below:

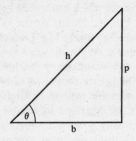

As an aid to memory we have labelled the sides b (base), p (perpendicular) and h (hypotenuse). The angle between p and b is a right angle, and θ is the angle we are looking at in detail. It is possible to imagine all the sides to be simultaneously doubled in length without changing the angles. This gives a triangle which in geometry is called *similar* to the starting triangle, and by considering a few such similar triangles we can see that the *ratios* b/h, p/b and p/h will be the same for them all and will depend only on the size of the angle θ. (Note, by the way, that in trigonometry a symbol such as p is often used as a name for the perpendicular and also as a mathematical symbol for the *length* of the perpendicular. This causes no problem, but it is precisely such notational problems which are taken very seriously in the study of symbolic logic.) The cosine, sine and tangent of the angle θ are defined as

$$\cos\theta = \frac{b}{h}; \ \sin\theta = \frac{p}{h}; \ \tan\theta = \frac{p}{b}.$$

(Remember that there is a sign outside a public house: if your son goes inside do not tan the poor boy!)

We clearly have the relationship $ph^{-1} = (pb^{-1})(bh^{-1})$, which becomes

$$\sin\theta = \cos\theta\tan\theta.$$

The *theorem of Pythagoras* tell us that

$$h^2 = p^2 + b^2,$$

which means that

$$1 = \frac{p^2}{h^2} + \frac{b^2}{h^2} = (\sin\theta)^2 + (\cos\theta)^2.$$

The abbreviations $\sin^2\theta$ and $\cos^2\theta$ are often used for $(\sin\theta)^2$ and $(\cos\theta)^2$.

When using a scientific calculator we first put in θ and then press the cos key, if we want $\cos\theta$. We have an immediate problem, since we have to decide on the units for θ. For example, a right angle can be called 90 degrees or $\frac{1}{2}\pi$ radians. A *radian* is a unit which we can describe by means of a diagram:

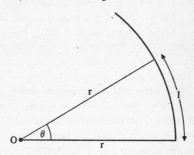

We draw a circle of radius r about the centre O, and then draw two radii with an angle θ between them, as shown. The distance l along the circle is then given by

$$l = r\theta$$

where θ is the angle in radians. Since the circumference of the circle is $2\pi r$, it follows that for a right angle we shall have

$$\frac{1}{4}.(2\pi r) = r\theta$$

so that a right angle is $\frac{1}{2}\pi$ radians. In scientific work some of the mathematical theory is easier if we use radians, and so most calculators have a switch which must be set to tell the calculator whether we mean 3.24 degrees or 3.24 radians when we put in the number 3.24 (for example). A few calculators also will work with grads (a right angle equals 100 grads). Because a scientific calculator has to do more things than a simple calculator it often has *dual-purpose* keys. For example, on the Sinclair Oxford 300 calculator, the symbol COS appears above the ordinary numerical key marked 8. A special function key must be pressed to tell the machine that it is the second (upper) use of the key which is required. On the Texas Instruments TI58 calculator the special key is actually marked 2ND. Suppose that we set $\theta = 1$ radian in the calculator, and press the cos key. We get 0.5403023. However, in some problems we might want to do a similar calculation backwards; for example, we might have the value of the ratio b/h (i.e., $\cos\theta$) and need θ. Most calculators will have a $[\![COS^{-1}]\!]$ or $[\![ARC\ COS]\!]$ key which gives us θ if we put in $\cos\theta$. To have separate $[\![COS^{-1}]\!]$, $[\![SIN^{-1}]\!]$ and $[\![TAN^{-1}]\!]$ keys is a little wasteful, so many calculators have one $[\![ARC]\!]$ key plus the $[\![COS]\!]$, $[\![SIN]\!]$ and $[\![TAN]\!]$ keys. To get $\cos^{-1}\theta$ we first enter θ and then press the keys $[\![ARC\ COS]\!]$. If we try working out $\cos\theta$ for gradually increasing θ values, we find that $\cos\theta$ is negative for angles between 90 and 270 degrees, but it never strays outside the region between 1 and -1. Accordingly, if we put 1.23 into the calculator and try to find $\cos^{-1}1.23$, we will get an error indication of some sort from the calculator, because we are asking the impossible; there is no angle which has a cosine equal to 1.23. A mathematician would say that the function $\cos^{-1}x$ is *not defined* at $x = 1.23$. Dealing with scientific calculators certainly teaches the user to think carefully about such important problems. Most calculator handbooks contain a list of instructions about the range of numbers which can be used to give sensible results for each of the function keys. There can arise problems with the simple $[\![COS]\!]$ key in some calculators if

θ is too big, but these can be avoided by noting that one complete turn is 360 degrees or 2π radians. So, if we have obtained an angle of 7324 degrees from some piece of arithmetic, we can reduce it to a physically sensible angle by subtracting whole turns. In a calculator with automatic arithmetic facilities we put in

$$[\![7324 \; - \; 360 \; = \; =]\!]$$

and press the $[\![=]\!]$ key until a number less than 360 appears. We get 124 degrees, and most scientific calculators will give cos 124 directly. On our first diagram we could only show θ as being an angle less than $90°$, but the rule for defining $\cos \theta$ for angles up to $180°$ is

$$\cos(180° - \theta) \; = \; -\cos \theta$$

so that $\cos 124° \; = \; -\cos 56°$. In our original diagram of the triangle, we can see that the sine of the angle opposite to θ is equal to the cosine of θ. However, by one of Euclid's theorems, all the three angles must add up to $180°$. This means that the angle opposite to θ is $90° - \theta$, so that

$$\sin(90° - \theta) \; = \; \cos \theta.$$

As an example of a calculation involving a large angle we could consider a wheel of radius 1 metre (and thus circumference 2π metres). If it rolls at 10 metres per second for 7 seconds, it has turned through $(7 \times 10) \div 2\pi$ revolutions, i.e., through 11.141 revolutions, which is also 4010.7 degrees. However, to find the height above the ground of the point which was initially at the top of the wheel, we can forget about the 11 whole turns and look at only the last 0.141 turn, i.e., 50.7 degrees. The height will be $1 + \cos 50.7° \; = \; 1.633$ metres. From the various relationships between $\cos \theta$, $\sin \theta$ and $\tan \theta$, it follows that if we are able to find $\cos \theta$, we can get $\sin \theta$ and $\tan \theta$ from it. It turns out that $\cos \theta$ is the easiest of the three functions to work out on a *simple* calculator, since, as we shall see later, we only need to enter θ once into a simple calculator to get $\cos \theta$. On a full scientific calculator, of course, only one entry of θ is needed for $\cos \theta$, $\sin \theta$ and $\tan \theta$; we say more about this in section 5.7.

4.3. The derivative of cos x

In using the calculus, the name x is traditionally used for a variable quantity, whereas the symbol θ is often used for angles in trigonometry. By now, it should cause the reader few problems if we speak of $\cos x$ rather than $\cos \theta$; the number (x or θ) must still be an angle if we are speaking about its cosine.

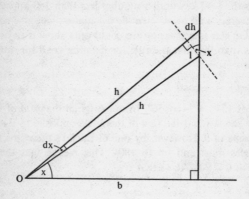

Consider the diagram, on which dx is a very tiny angle added to the angle x. The dashed circle is of radius h with centre at O. By using the definition of an angle in radians and thinking of l as a little portion of the circle, we have

$$l = h\,dx$$

with dx in radians. Also, from the definition of a cosine we have the equation

$$\cos(x+dx) = b(h+dh)^{-1}$$
$$= \frac{b}{h}\left(1+\frac{dh}{h}\right)^{-1}.$$

Since $1+(dh/h)$ is close to 1 we can use our results about powers of numbers close to 1 (section 3.5). We thus get

$$\cos(x+dh) = \frac{b}{h}\left(1-\frac{dh}{h}\right).$$

From the triangle with sides dh and l we also have

$$dh = l \tan x = h \tan x \, dx.$$

(To see that the angle involved equals x we must use the fact that the angles in a triangle add up to 180°, as do the three angles at the point where l intersects the perpendicular side.) Combining the last two equations gives the result

$$\cos(x+dx) = \frac{b}{h} - \frac{b}{h^2} dh$$
$$= \cos x - \sin x \, dx.$$

According to our definition of a derivative in section 3.16, this means that the derivative of $\cos x$ is $-\sin x$. By a simple argument (exercise 1) we find also that the derivative of $\sin x$ is $\cos x$, but it is important to note that these results are true only if x is an angle given in radians. (See why by checking through the argument again.) The *second* derivative of $\cos x$ is thus $-\cos x$. These results are easy to remember (even if the geometrical proof is not!). They can be *used* to great advantage, as we shall see in what follows, so do not worry if you cannot digest their proofs fully at a first reading. Even in mathematics it is often useful to read a work quickly to get the 'feel' of it, before filling in all the details of the proofs.

4.4. Power series

In section 4.3 we looked at the derivatives of things which do not look like polynomials, whereas we only looked at derivatives of powers of x in section 3.16. One of the most fruitful mathematical tricks is to write a function as a series of powers even when we did not first think of it in that way. The series we get is usually an extended polynomial, that is, it has an *infinite* number of terms. Thus, let us just suppose that we can represent $\cos x$ as follows:

$$\cos x = a_0 + a_2 x^2 + a_4 x^4 + \dots$$

We know how to find the first and second derivatives of a power of x, and so we must have the result (on finding the first derivative)

$$-\sin x = 2a_2 x + 4a_4 x^3 + \ldots$$

since we already know that $\cos x$ has $-\sin x$ as its derivative. Taking the derivative again gives, since $-\cos x$ is the second derivative of $\cos x$,

$$-\cos x = 2a_2 + 12a_4 x^2 + \ldots$$

If this last result is to be consistent with our first guess for $\cos x$ (for *any* value of x) we must have

$$-2a_2 = a_0; \quad -12a_4 = a_2; \text{ etc.}$$

By looking at our original diagram we can see that for a very small angle $\cos x$ must be 1, since the base and hypotenuse of the triangle will be of virtually equal length. This means that we must set $a_0 = 1$ to make our guess fit at $x = 0$. Knowing a_0 we can get a_2, then a_4, and so on, and arrive at the results

$$\cos x = 1 - \frac{1}{2}x^2 + \frac{1}{24}x^4 - \frac{1}{720}x^6 + \ldots$$

$$\sin x = x - \frac{1}{6}x^3 + \frac{1}{120}x^5 - \ldots$$

These *power series expansions* for $\cos x$ and $\sin x$ are very useful, and similar expansions can be found for many functions which appear in scientific work. There is one problem which the astute reader should have seen in the argument above: why did we not have terms with x, x^3 (i.e., odd powers) in our guess for $\cos x$? Well, we stuck to one of the conventions of traditional trigonometry, namely that

$$\cos(-x) = \cos x; \quad \sin(-x) = -\sin x.$$

To ensure this, we must have only even powers in $\cos x$ and odd powers in $\sin x$. Although the series for $\cos x$ is infinite we can still use it to get good values for $\cos x$ without working out all the terms (which is literally impossible, of course!). For example, at $x = 0.2$ (one fifth of a radian) the term $(1/720)x^6$, which follows $(1/24)x^4$, is about 10^{-7}, and so taking only the terms up to x^4 gives us a very good answer indeed.

If we have only a simple calculator we can get a good estimate of $\cos x$ for small x by condensing the terms up to x^4 into a single expression

$$\cos x = \frac{1}{24}[(x^2 - 6)^2 - 12]$$

which, as we recall from section 3.8, needs only one entry of x. Setting $x = 1$, for an angle of 1 radian (or about 57 degrees), gives the estimate 0.54167 for cos 1, whereas 0.54030 is an accurate value to five figures. To get an even better estimate we use the 'angle doubling' formula

$$\cos 2x = 2\cos^2 x - 1.$$

The reader who has not met this result before can obtain it by squaring the series for $\cos x$ and seeing that the result fits (we also look at this result in section 4.13). Accordingly, we can get a good answer by working out $\cos \frac{1}{2}$ first and then using the doubling formula to get cos 1. (Note that this is yet another example of the kind of process outlined in exercise 8 of Chapter 3.) We find, using a simple calculator, and our simple formula for $\cos x$,

$$\cos \tfrac{1}{2} = 0.87760 \rightarrow \cos 1 = 0.54038.$$

Starting at $\cos \frac{1}{4}$ and doing the doubling process twice gives

$$0.968913 \rightarrow 0.877583 \rightarrow 0.540307$$

whereas cos 1 = 0.540302 to six figures. We see that it is not difficult to get a value for $\cos x$ which is as good as or better than that obtained from five-figure tables. To find $\sin x$ we could devise an analogous approach for the $\sin x$ series, although it would have the slight disadvantage of requiring two entries of x:

$$\sin x = \frac{x}{120}[(x^2 - 10)^2 + 20].$$

More simply, we can just find $\cos x$ and then calculate $\sin x$ as $\sqrt{(1 - \cos^2 x)}$, assuming that we have a square root key.

As a simple example of the use of cosines we can consider the case of a yacht which is 'tacking', that is, moving in a zig-zag course to use the wind, while trying to move on average towards the east.

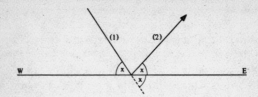

To find how many sea miles to the east the yacht moves in an hour we must multiply the actual speed in knots (sea miles per hour) by cos x, if we consider part (2) of the motion. Now, on part (1) this easterly motion is still the same, but the forward direction of motion makes an angle −x with the easterly direction, as we see by studying the dotted line. Similarly, if we imagine the yacht motion reversed on section (1), its forward motion would make an angle 180° − x with the easterly direction, and it would have a *negative* easterly speed (since it would be going to the west). In this case and in many other physical problems it is clear that the properties $\cos(-x) = \cos x$ and $\cos(\pi - x) = -\cos x$ have a definite physical interpretation.

4.5. Some uses for sines and cosines

Consider the triangle shown below, with sides of lengths a, b and c:

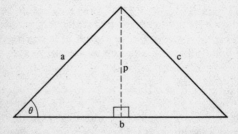

It is *not* a right-angled triangle, but we can artificially make one by drawing in line p which is perpendicular to the base. The area of the triangle is given by the product $\frac{1}{2}$ × base length × perpendicular height, i.e., $\frac{1}{2}bp$. However, this can also be written as $\frac{1}{2}ba \sin \theta$, since we know that in the right-angled triangle we have the relationship $p = a \sin \theta$. Thus we can find the area of the triangle by using the lengths of two sides and the sine of the angle between them. Suppose now that we call the base lengths of the two right-angled triangles l and r (left and right), so that $l + r = b$. Using the Pythagoras theorem twice, once in each triangle, we find

$$
\begin{aligned}
c^2 &= r^2 + (a^2 - l^2) \\
&= a^2 + (r + l)(r - l) \\
&= a^2 + b(b - 2l) \\
&= a^2 + b^2 - 2ab \cos \theta.
\end{aligned}
$$

(The reader is invited to follow through the algebra, filling in one or two steps which we have not displayed.) The resulting *cosine formula*, as it is usually called, is a kind of generalized form of the Pythagoras theorem. If we set θ equal to $90°$ (i.e. $\pi/2$), we have $\cos \theta = 0$ and $c^2 = a^2 + b^2$, which is the Pythagoras theorem. Further, we can see from the cosine formula that doubling the lengths of a and b, with θ fixed, gives a doubled value for c, so that the lengths of the sides all increase correctly in a 2:1 ratio.

When a ray of light passes from one material to another (e.g., air to glass) we have this situation:

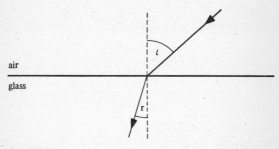

The relationship between the angle of incidence ι and the angle of refraction r is

$$\sin \iota = \mu \sin r.$$

The number μ is the *refractive index* of the glass (strictly speaking of glass with respect to air), and is a number greater than 1, up to 1.5 for some glasses. As the reader may check on a scientific calculator and by looking at the definition, the sine of an angle never exceeds 1 in value. Thus if we try to get $\sin^{-1} 1.2$ (i.e. the angle which has a sine of 1.2) on a scientific calculator, we get an error indication from the calculator. Now, if we put a value of r into the equation for which $\mu \sin r$ is greater than 1, we can't find an angle ι which fits the equation. Thus, no ι value will make the light pass into the glass at an angle of refraction greater than that angle for which $\sin r = \mu^{-1}$. If the light is going the other way, from glass to air, any ray approaching the boundary at an angle such that $\sin r > \mu^{-1}$ will not be able to escape from the glass. It will be reflected back into the glass again, that is, the surface will act as a mirror for it. By varying the angle at which the rays of light are viewed it is possible to determine at what angle this internal reflection begins to happen, and thus to calculate the refractive index μ of the glass. The bending of light rays means, for example, that a stick with one end under water appears to be bent, while if we look straight down from above at something under water, it has an apparent depth equal to the true depth divided by the refractive index μ of water.

The sine function also appears in the *sine formula* for a triangle:

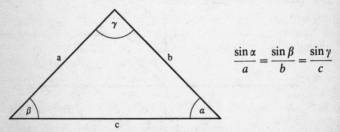

$$\frac{\sin \alpha}{a} = \frac{\sin \beta}{b} = \frac{\sin \gamma}{c}$$

The sine and cosine formulae can be used together to simplify calculations. Suppose we have $a = 2$, $b = 3$, $c = 4$ and want to find α, β and γ. From the cosine rule we have

$$2^2 = 3^2 + 4^2 - (2 \times 3 \times 4)\cos \alpha$$

which gives

$$\cos \alpha = \frac{21}{24} = 0.8750.$$

We can use the cosine rule again to get $\cos \beta$ *or* we can use the sine rule:

$$\sin \beta = \frac{b}{a} \times \sin \alpha$$

$$= \frac{3}{2} \times \sqrt{1-(0.875)^2} = 0.7262.$$

Using the $[\![ARC\ COS]\!]$ and $[\![ARC\ SIN]\!]$ keys on a scientific calculator we find $\alpha = 28.96°$, $\beta = 46.57°$. To get γ we remember that the three angles add up to $180°$, so $\gamma = 104.47°$. By taking the two shorter sides first, we avoided having to deal with an obtuse angle (one greater than $90°$) until the last step of the calculation.

4.6. Compound interest. Exponentials

Let us suppose that a sum s is invested for one year at a rate of $i\%$ interest. The total sum at the end of the year is the initial amount plus the interest:

$$s+\frac{i}{100}s = s\left(1+\frac{i}{100}\right).$$

In a compound interest system the interest in the second year will be paid on the sum at the start of that year, which includes the interest for the first year. The total amount left will be

$$s\left(1+\frac{i}{100}\right)\left(1+\frac{i}{100}\right)$$

and after n years the total will be sR^n, if we introduce the short symbol R for the constant number $(1+i/100)$. On a simple calculator we can find the total after one, two, three years etc. by the key strokes

$$[\![s\ \times\ R\ =\ =]\!]\ \ldots$$

We have already done some compound interest calculations in section 2.5, but now we look at one which involves root extraction. We ask what interest rate would be needed to make £1000 grow to £1500 in five years. We require that R^5 shall be 1.5, i.e., we want the (real) fifth root of 1.5. On a simple calculator we can find the root by the methods of Chapter 2. On a scientific calculator we use the key strokes $[\![\,1.5\ \ y^x\ \ 0.2\ \ =\,]\!]$ (or $[\![\,1.5\ \ y^x\ \ 5\ \ 1/x\ \ =\,]\!]$ on some machines which will work out $\frac{1}{5} = 0.2$ before taking the power) to get $R = 1.0845$, so that the required interest rate is 8.45%.

If $100r\%$ is added to the starting amount *every six months*, the effective annual interest rate is greater than $200r\%$. If we call this effective annual rate $100a$, the annual multiplying factor is $(1 + a)$. However it is also $(1 + r)^2$, since the six-monthly factor is applied twice. We must have

$$(1 + r)^2 = 1 + a.$$

Now, suppose we want the value of a to be 0.10 (i.e., 10%). What value of r is needed? We must have

$$1 + r = \sqrt{1.1} = \pm 1.049.$$

The $\pm$ (plus or minus) sign is used because both the positive and negative numbers are square roots of 1.1 (section 3.15). Two values of r are obtained, $r = 0.049$ and $r = -2.049$. The solution $r = 0.049$ (4.9%) is the one which makes 'common sense'; adding 4.9% every six months amounts to adding 10% per year, not 9.8% per year. (In such a situation, most British banks would describe the annual rate as 10%, some American ones would describe it as 9.8%.) The solution $r = -2.049$ makes 'mathematical sense', but would not correspond to real banking policy. Thus, if the bank multiplied the depositor's initial sum by the factor $1 + r = -1.049$ every six months, it would indeed multiply it by 1.10 in a year, but after the first six months the depositor would owe the bank money! This example shows how, when an argument leads to a mathematical equation, we must check whether the solutions to the equation make sense in terms of the original problem.

Suppose now that we can have our money increased by 10% every year, by 5% every six months, or by $2\frac{1}{2}\%$ every three months. It seems clear that we get the most at the end of the year by the third process. In fact the multiplying factors are

$$(1.1)^1, \qquad (1.05)^2, \qquad (1.025)^4$$

i.e.,   1.1000,   1.1025,   1.1038

and we can see that there seems to be a 'diminishing return' setting in. If we consider a hypothetical process in which the factor $(1+1/10n)$ is used n times a year we get the annual multiplying factor

$$\left(1+\frac{0.1}{n}\right)^n.$$

This factor takes the following typical values (with n in brackets), as worked out on an eight-figure calculator:

(64) 1.1050811   (256) 1.1051301   (1024) 1.1050742.

The value at $n = 1024$ is clearly wrong, since the true value should increase with n; it is the rounding error (see section 1.6) in the calculator which is producing this error. On a more accurate (eleven-figure) calculator the results are

(64) 1.1050847   (256) 1.1051493   (1024) 1.1051655.

We can see that as n increases the result appears to be tending towards some value, about 1.1052, which is called the *limit* of the result as n tends to infinity. Any number x could be used in place of 0.1, and the limiting number obtained varies with x, i.e., is a *function* of x. The *exponential function* $\exp x$ is defined as follows (with Lt meaning limit):

$$\exp x = \operatorname*{Lt}_{n \to \infty}\left(1+\frac{x}{n}\right)^n$$

and our results here give $\exp 0.1 \simeq 1.1052$. The exact value is 1.10517 to five figures. We have seen how $\cos x$ and $\sin x$ could be expressed as power series; $\exp x$ can be similarly treated, if we start from another way of defining it:

derivative of $\exp x = \exp x$.

That this *does* define the same function as the limit we can see roughly as follows. If at time t we have the amount $x(t)$, and at very slightly later time $t + h$ we have amount $x(t + h)$, we know that

$$x(t+h) = x(t)+[h \times \text{derivative of } x(t)].$$

However, if we suppose that the amount is being continuously increased by a compound interest mechanism, we expect that the increase in the amount over the tiny time interval h will be proportional to the time elapsed (h) and to the initial amount $x(t)$. We can thus express it as $khx(t)$, where k is some constant. The particular choice $k = 1$ gives us the particular function $x(t)$ called $\exp t$, and we see that $\exp t$ must equal its own derivative. Of course, using the name x instead of t for the varying quantity does not change things. We now try to get a power series which represents $\exp x$. Using the same kind of argument as in section 4.4, we see that the series *must* be

$$\exp x = 1 + x + \tfrac{1}{2}x^2 + \tfrac{1}{6}x^3 + \dots$$

in order for the derivative of the series to equal the series. By squaring the series for $\exp x$ we obtain the series

$$\begin{aligned}
(\exp x)^2 &= (1 + x + \tfrac{1}{2}x^2 + \tfrac{1}{6}x^3 + \dots)^2 \\
&= 1 + 2x + 2x^2 + \dots \\
&= 1 + 2x + \tfrac{1}{2}.(2x)^2 + \dots \\
&= \exp 2x.
\end{aligned}$$

Now, this is precisely the way in which we expect powers of some number to behave, since the law of indices gives

$$(y^x)^2 = y^{(x+x)} = y^{2x}.$$

We also find $\exp(-x) = (\exp x)^{-1}$, and these results suggest that we may have

$$\exp x = e^x$$

for some number e. This is so, and we can find what the number e is, since we have

$$e^1 = \exp 1 = 1 + 1 + \tfrac{1}{2} + \tfrac{1}{6} + \dots$$

The value of this sum is 2.71828 to five figures. A scientific calculator has a key to give $\exp x$, and also one to give the inverse function $\ln x$; $\ln x$, the *natural logarithm* of x is defined as follows: if $\exp x = y$, then $x = \ln y$.

The law of radioactive decay involves the exponential function. If we start with n atoms of a radioactive element, after t years there will be $n \exp(-kt)$ atoms left, where k is a constant characteristic of the particular type of atom. The *half-life* is the time after which half of the atoms of that type remain (the atoms are not destroyed; they change into atoms of a different type, which might also be radioactive). The half-life is thus defined as the time value for which

$$\tfrac{1}{2}n = n\exp(-kt)$$

i.e., $2 = [\exp(-kt)]^{-1} = \exp(kt)$.

Since $\exp(0.69315) = 2$, we find that $t = 0.69315k^{-1}$ gives us the half-life, which we call T. Now, after time $2T$, have the atoms all gone? No, because their number is $n\exp(-2T)$, which is just $\exp(-T)$ times the number at time T. This means that there are $n \times \tfrac{1}{2} \times \tfrac{1}{2} = \tfrac{1}{4}n$ atoms left after time $2T$. Analogously, after a time of x half-lives, there will be a fraction $(\tfrac{1}{2})^x$ of the original atoms left. Thus, if the half-life is one thousand years, there will still be 10% of the atoms left (producing 10% of the initial radioactivity) after a time given by

$$0.1 = \exp(-kt).$$

This becomes

$$10 = \exp(kt)$$

on taking reciprocals on both sides, since $\exp kt$ and $\exp(-kt)$ are reciprocals of one another. Remembering that the natural log, ln, is defined so that $\ln y = x$ if $y = \exp x$, we must have

$$\ln 10 = kt = 0.69315\, T^{-1}t$$
$$= 2.3026$$

where a scientific calculator gives us $\ln 10$. With $T = 1000$ years, we get $t = 3322$ years from this calculation, so that 3322 years are needed for the radioactivity to get down to 10% of its initial value.

4.7. Decibels

Most scientific calculators will give both the natural log and $\log_{10}$ of a number. Logs to the base 10 are not as often used in basic scientific theory as are natural logs (to the base $e = 2.7182818\ldots$), but they are used in scales concerned with the *ratios* of quantities in electrical engineering. The simple method for producing values of 10^x using the square root key (section 2.2) can be useful for simple calculations of this type.

The basic defining formula for the decibel scale is

$$\text{Decibels} = 10 \log_{10}\left(\frac{p_2}{p_1}\right)$$

where p_2 and p_1 are the *powers* of two sources to be compared. For example, if an electrical signal generator has a switch marked '20 db attenuator', this means that turning the switch will attenuate (i.e., decrease) the output. Since we have the result $10^2 = 100$, it follows that $2 = \log_{10}(100)$ and so 20 db attenuation means that the power is cut down to $\frac{1}{100}$ of its original value. The comparison makes sense for a signal generator only if it is supplying current to some *fixed* load (e.g., a resistance across its terminals) which is not changed when the attenuator is turned on. The *voltage* across the resistor, as measured on an oscilloscope, would then fall in the ratio $10:1$ (*not* $100:1$), because the power dissipated in the resistance varies as the square of the voltage. A power ratio of 100 corresponds to a voltage ratio of 10. Since the decibel scale is concerned with *ratios* of quantities, it is not quite correct to use decibels as 'absolute' units. For example, to say that an aeroplane gives a noise level of 90 decibels requires that we have some standard sound level (agreed on by all) which is used to set up the decibel scale. The air pressure in a sound wave (of a given frequency) oscillates, as does the voltage in an A.C. circuit (section 3.14), and the power carried by the wave depends on the square of the peak pressure. It is the air pressure which is usually taken as the variable to consider, so that (as for voltage) a 20 db increase in sound level at some frequency means a $10:1$ ratio of air pressure, a 10 db increase means a $10^{\frac{1}{2}}:1$ pressure ratio, and so on. If the threshold level of noise for human hearing is used to give the zero point on the scale (i.e., 0 db), then this corresponds to a pressure of 2×10^{-5} Newtons per square metre. Of course, this threshold represents a rough average for 'normal' human subjects; the threshold of hearing for a group of such subjects might well vary between ± 10 db on this scale, and for a given subject it will vary somewhat with the sound frequency (no dogs allowed!). By testing fifty-two young people, first while they had catarrhal infection and then when they had recovered, R. W. Fearn (*Journal of Sound and Vibration*, Vol. 46, p. 291) concluded that on average a cold causes a temporary hearing loss of about 3 db. This means that the hearing threshold *rises* by 3 db. He also found that swimming causes a temporary hearing loss of about 5 db for a day or so. In an article in the *Lancet* for 2 August 1975, Dr R. Hanson and R. W. Fearn pointed out that, although continuous sound levels above 90 dbA were regarded as probably harmful under working conditions, such levels are often exceeded at the 'pop' concerts which are frequently attended by young people. (The dbA is a kind of averaged decibel measured by a meter which simulates the frequency response of the human ear.) While industrial noise is most likely to affect hearing ability at the higher frequencies, it seems that loud musical 'noise' (perhaps older readers would say 'musical' noise) can affect hearing ability over a range of frequencies. Hanson and Fearn's results (and also others which they have obtained more recently) suggest that young people who regularly listen to loud amplified 'pop' music can suffer a hearing loss of around 10 db.

In both the cases which we have discussed above the *power ratio* is the basic quantity involved in the decibel formula, but the quantity x to be measured (voltage or pressure) is such that power is proportional to x^2. In these circumstances, then, the basic formula becomes

$$\text{Decibels} = 10 \log_{10}\left(\frac{p_2}{p_1}\right) = 20 \log_{10}\left(\frac{x_2}{x_1}\right)$$

and the reader is advised to check whether the author of any particular work using decibels is using a factor of 10 or 20 in his basic formula. For example, workers on the hearing loss problem mentioned above might use the symbol p to mean pressure, whereas we have used it to mean power. When comparing two different sound sources, say two aeroplanes of 103 and 88 dbA, without knowing the 0dbA level, we use the principle that *dividing* numbers means *subtracting* logs. This gives

$$103 - 88 = 15 = 10 \log_{10}\left(\frac{p_2}{p_1}\right)$$

so that the power ratio for the two sounds is $10^{\frac{3}{2}}$, about 32. A simple calculator gives

$[\![10 \ \times \ = \ = \ \sqrt{\ }]\!]$ $\boxed{31.62277}$.

This result certainly does not mean that one sound appears 32 times as loud as the other. It will seem less than twice as loud to a human listener, and we shall say a little more about this when we look at power laws in the next section. (Do not confuse the two different uses of the word 'power' in this context!)

4.8. Power laws

Scientific calculators have a powering key $[\![x^y]\!]$ which will find the yth power of x, where y is any real number and x is any real positive number. The key strokes used to find, for example, $(3.027)^{5.23}$ are

$[\![3.027 \ x^y \ 5.23 \ =]\!]$ $\boxed{327.86493}$.

(On a few calculators the numbers x and y are entered in the reverse order.) There are many examples in scientific work of quantities which obey power law relationships. We have seen various examples throughout the book of laws of the type

$b = ka^n$.

Here a and b are the variables concerned and k and n are constants. In the case $n = 1$ we say that b is *directly proportional* to a; in the case $n = -1$ we say that b is *inversely proportional* to a. For the cases $n = -1$, 1, or 2, or the case $n = \frac{5}{4}$ of section 3.12, we can work out the powers of a on a simple calculator. It is only for more 'peculiar' power laws that we need the general $[\![x^y]\!]$ key of the scientific calculator. Experimental psychology provides several examples of such power laws, particularly those relating to the subjective judgement of magnitudes such as the strength of a light source or a sound source. The basic law which governs most such subjective judgements is the *Weber–Fechner law*, which says that the just noticeable difference in some stimulus is proportional to the size of the stimulus. In other words, a stimulus must change by some definite *percentage* before we can detect the change, and each kind of stimulus has its own characteristic percentage. This law, which fits quite well to experimental results, leads to a power law type relation between response and stimulus. J. R. Greeno, in his book *Elementary Theoretical Psychology*, gives an account of various experimental results which illustrate this power law relationship. For example, the brightness of a light source can be taken to be proportional to the power supplied to the source if we want a scientific measure, but the brightness as judged by the human eye obeys a law of form:

Judged brightness $= k(\text{physical brightness})^{0.5}$.

This is (probably by coincidence) a square root law, although it must be remembered that such results refer to carefully controlled experimental situations, and can only be taken as rough approximations if we apply them to everyday experience. With this proviso, we can also quote the law relating to the judgement of sound strength:

Judged sound strength $= k(\text{pressure})^{0.3}$.

Here the air pressure in the sound wave is the quantity usually measured on the decibel scale (see section 4.7); with power taken as proportional to $(\text{pressure})^2$ it follows that judged sound strength will vary roughly as $(\text{power})^{0.15}$. A judged sound ratio of 2:1 goes with a power ratio of $2^{6.67}:1$, i.e., 102:1. This is only approximate, since there is a frequency dependence in the ear's sensitivity, and experimental 'laws' usually refer to single pure tones, often at the standard frequency of 1000 cycles per second. Nevertheless, the calculation above helps to explain why transistor radios can still produce an acceptable (or somewhat unacceptable) noise level using only small batteries as a power source.

   Power law relationships can often be made to look like linear relationships if we use logarithms (to any base). Thus the two formulae

$b = ka^n$

and

$\log b = \log k + n \log a$

say the same thing, but the second one is more useful if we have some measured values of *a* and *b* and want to check whether they *are* related by a power law. If we draw a graph of log *b* versus log *a* we will get a straight line, with slope *n* and intercept log *k*.

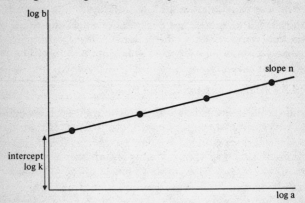

Of course we won't expect a *perfect* line by plotting experimental results, but to confirm a power law behaviour we would need the 'scatter' of the points around the straight line to be small.

4.9. A bit of information

If we toss a coin repeatedly we expect to get heads on about half of the throws, and if we write down the result of a sequence of throws we get a row of symbols:

HTTHTH...   or   100101...

if we represent heads by 1 and tails by 0. The numerical way of writing down the result gives us a number in binary notation, of the type which is used in most electronic computing devices. After three throws, for example, a result of 111 would indicate three heads, while 000 would indicate three tails. 111 is the binary form of 7, and the three throws give some number from 0 to 7. This represents eight different possibilities; since we can have two different outcomes per throw, the number of different possible outcomes after three throws is $2 \times 2 \times 2 = 2^3 = 8$. Similarly, if we throw a die, with numbers on it from 1 to 6, we can represent the results by a number in base 6 (if we subtract 1 from the number on the die), and after three throws we could have obtained $6^3 = 216$ different numbers. The number 555 in base 6 represents 215 in base 10, and we can obtain numbers between 0 and 215.

Suppose that we think of the sequence 100101 ... produced by the coin throwing as a message which is being transmitted. If we know that each symbol is equally likely to be a 1 or a 0, the *information content* of each symbol is defined to be 1 bit (short for binary digit). In other words, one bit of information is produced when we make a definite choice between two equally likely alternatives. This definition of information is used in statistical information theory, and it essentially takes 'information' to mean 'removal of uncertainty'. For example, if we look at two symbols in our binary code message, we could have four different possibilities; if we look at three symbols we could have eight possibilities. Thus, the number of possible messages doubles every time we add a digit. However, if we already know the previous symbols, we are really only choosing between two possible messages as each symbol arrives, so we could regard each symbol as conveying an equal amount of information (i.e., one bit). The technical definition of the information per symbol is as follows:

i (in bits) = $-$(sum of $p \log_2 p$ values).

Here the symbol p is the probability associated with each *possible* digit, and $\log_2 p$ is the log to base 2 of that number p. Thus, for our binary code message we could get 0 or 1 at each step, and each has probability $\frac{1}{2}$. The sum required is then $\frac{1}{2}\log_2(\frac{1}{2}) + \frac{1}{2}\log_2(\frac{1}{2})$, or $\log_2(\frac{1}{2})$. Since we know that $2^{-1} = \frac{1}{2}$, it follows that $\log_2(\frac{1}{2}) = -1$. The minus sign in the formula for i then removes the minus from -1, leaving $i = 1$ bit as the result. If we think of the message as made up of 'pair symbols', taking two digits at a time as the basic symbol, then each 'symbol' can take four forms, each of probability $\frac{1}{4}$. The sum is then over four possibilities, and we find

$$i = -4(\frac{1}{4}\log_2 \frac{1}{4}) = 2$$

since $2^{-2} = 4$. We emphasize that this simple calculation supposes that each symbol is chosen independently, with no regard to the choice for the preceding symbol. If there were such a link we would have to take an i value *per pair* of symbols and halve it to get an average i value per symbol. In our simple calculation above i is proportional to the length of the 'symbol'; the logarithm term in the formula is the one responsible for this.

Most calculators (even scientific ones) cannot give logs to base 2, but a prescription such as $\log_2 x = 1.4427 \log_e x$ can be used. On a simple calculator with a squaring operation we can get a fair estimate, as follows. To find $\log_2 6$ we note that $6 = 4 \times 1.5$, so that we only need to deal with the 1.5 and then add 2 to the log afterwards. Thus we can always suppose that we start from a number between 1 and 2. The prescription is as follows, with d meaning 'displayed number':

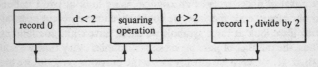

Starting from 1.5 we get the result:

Operation	Display	Recorded number
$[\![x^2]\!]$	2.25	1
$[\![\div 2]\!]$	1.125	
$[\![x^2]\!]$	1.265625	0
$[\![x^2]\!]$	1.6018066	0
$[\![x^2]\!]$	2.5657843	1
$[\![\div 2]\!]$	1.2828921	
$[\![x^2]\!]$	1.6458121	0

and so on. The author worked out the above prescription after some careful study, but the reader should be able to see where it came from if he is given the following clue: the point of the calculation is to write the initial number as a product of various roots of 2. The recorded number column shows that

$$1.5 = \left\{ \begin{matrix} 2^{\frac{1}{2}} \times 1 \times 1 & \times 2^{\frac{1}{16}} \times 1 \times \ldots \\ 1 \quad\ 0 \quad\ 0 & 1 \quad\ 0 \quad \ldots \end{matrix} \right\}.$$

The calculation if extended further gives the sequence 1001010111000 and leads to the following sum for $\log_2(1.5)$:

$$\log_2(1.5) = \frac{1}{2} + \frac{1}{16} + \frac{1}{64} + \frac{1}{256} + \frac{1}{512} + \ldots$$
$$= 0.5850 \quad \text{(to four places)}.$$

To work out the sum on a calculator with an $[\![M+]\!]$ memory key and automatic K constant we can use the key strokes

$$[\![. \; 5 \; M+ \; \div \; 2 \; = \; = \; = \; M+ \; = \; = \; M+]\!] \ldots$$

and so on. The operation $\div 2$ is repeated by the $[\![=]\!]$ key and the intermediate $[\![M+]\!]$ key strokes do *not* interfere with this K constant operation. Alternatively, with no memory or K constant, we can simply make use of the following sequence, which adds $1/N$ to the displayed number,

$$[\![\times \; N \; + \; 1 \; \div \; N \; =]\!].$$

To check that $2^{0.5850}$ is close to 1.5 we have to multiply together the various powers of 2 which we have used to build up 1.5. This needs a memory and a square root key, which were not needed for the preceding parts of the calculation. The direct check provided by the $[\![y^x]\!]$ key on the Sinclair Enterprise Programmable calculator is $2^{0.5850} = 1.500039$. That calculator also gives the result for $\log_2 1.5$ by using the following key sequence

$$[\![1.5 \; \Delta \; 1nx \; \div \; 2 \; \Delta \; 1nx \; =]\!] \quad \boxed{0.58496}.$$

(The Δ stroke selects the second use of the dual purpose keys.) The basic principle behind this key stroke sequence is that

$$\log_e x = (\log_2 x) \times (\log_e 2).$$

On a simple calculator with a square root function it is quicker and still fairly accurate to use the result

$$\log_N x = 1nx \div 1nN$$

together with the following formula, valid for small x, which we treat in the next section:

$$1n(1+x) = x - \tfrac{1}{2}x^2 + \ldots$$
$$= -\tfrac{1}{2}[(x-1)^2 - 1].$$

For example, to find $1n1.5$ we use the square root key repeatedly until 1.5 is reduced to around 1.001:

$[\![1.5 \quad \sqrt{\ }]\!]$ (8 times) $\boxed{1.001585}$.

This number is our $(1 + x)$ value, so we use the key strokes

$[\![- 2 = x^2 - 1 \div 2 \pm =]\!]$ $\boxed{0.0015837}$.

We now multiply by 2 repeatedly 'to get back to where we started'.

$[\![\times 2 =]\!]$ (8 times) $\boxed{0.4054272}$.

$1n1.5$ is actually 0.40546 to five places. Treating $1n2$ by the above procedure gives $1n2 = 0.6930944$; the accurate result is 0.69314 to five places. The two results for the natural logs are both a little low, but their *ratio* is quite accurate and gives 0.58496, which is the value of $\log_2(1.5)$ correct to five figures. If a number is greater than $e = 2.7182818$, it can be divided repeatedly by e to make it less than e, so that the $1n$ process has an improved accuracy. Proceeding in this way we find, for example,

$$1n3 \quad \to \ 1.09844 \qquad \text{(low)}$$
$$1n10 \quad \to \ 2.30236 \qquad \text{(low)}$$

Ratio, $\log_{10}3 \to 0.47709$ (0.4771) (correct to 4 figures).

4.10. Simple methods for $\exp x$ and $\ln x$

For small x, $\exp x$ will be given quite closely by the first three terms in its series, which we can convert to a form which requires only one entry of x on a simple calculator. We have

$$1 + x + \tfrac{1}{2}x^2 = \tfrac{1}{2}[(x + 1)^2 + 1].$$

For this to be accurate x must be small, so we must use our 'round the houses' method again. Suppose we want $\exp(0.712)$. We divide 0.712 by 2 repeatedly to make it very small. Numerical experimentation shows that a value between 0.01 and 0.02 gives optimum results, and we have

$$(0.712)2^{-6} = 0.011125.$$

Applying the simple formula then gives $\exp(0.011125) = 1.0111868$. To get back to $\exp(0.712)$ we square the result six times, and find

2.03802; the accurate result to five figures is 2.03806. Another simple formula is

$$\exp x = \frac{(x+3)^2 + 3}{(x-3)^2 + 3}$$

but this requires two entries of x, or the use of a memory with a memory exchange key. Using this formula instead of the single-entry one leads to the estimate $\exp(0.712) = 2.03806$, if we proceed as we did before, that is, first work out $\exp(0.011125)$ and then square the result six times. Thus the second formula for $\exp x$ is more accurate even if less simple. To check that the trick of 'making x small' is necessary, the reader may see for himself what happens if we put $x = 0.712$ into the two formulae above. The resulting estimates (1.96547 and 2.03753) for $\exp x$ are not so good, although they still show the superior accuracy of the second formula. Our trial number 0.712 is less than 1; if we require a quantity such as $\exp(3.712)$ we can proceed by finding $\exp(0.712)$ and then multiplying the result by $\exp 3 = (2.7182818)^3$. The value of e is not difficult to remember and its use simplifies the calculation.

In traditional calculus it is possible to find an infinite series of powers of x which gives the natural logarithm of $1 + x$, $\ln(1 + x)$. We have seen that $\cos x$ and e^x have simple properties in terms of their first and second derivatives in the calculus. Leaving the proof to exercise 11, we note that $\ln(1 + x)$ has the property that its derivative equals the reciprocal of $(1 + x)$, i.e. $(1 + x)^{-1}$. If we proceed as before, we have to find a series such that its derivative gives a series for $(1 + x)^{-1}$. The argument of section 3.5 gave us a series for $(1 + x)^{-1}$, namely

$$(1 + x)^{-1} = 1 - x + x^2 - x^3 \ldots$$

and so we can see that the $\ln(1 + x)$ series would have to be

$$\ln(1 + x) = x - \tfrac{1}{2}x^2 + \tfrac{1}{3}x^3 \ldots$$

(Since $\ln(1) = 0$ we do not need a constant term to start off the series.)

We can treat this series in the same way as we did the others. It turns out that one efficient formula for x close to 1 is

$$\ln x = \frac{3(x^2 - 1)}{(x+2)^2 - 3}$$

while a simple single-entry formula is not so good. At $x = 1.2$ the formula gives $\ln(1.2) = 0.182322$, whereas the accurate result is 0.182320 to six figures. When dealing with a larger number, the square root is taken n times to get down to around 1.1, the formula is used, and the result is doubled n times to get the final result.

4.11. Inverse functions

If we have the result $y = \cos x$, we also write $x = \cos^{-1} y$, and refer to $\cos^{-1}$ as the inverse function of cos. Similarly, $\sin^{-1}$ is the inverse function of sin, and ln is the inverse function of exp. Suppose now that we start from the formula for $\cos x$ (with x small):

$$\cos x = \frac{1}{24}[(x^2 - 6)^2 - 12]$$

but suppose that we *know* $\cos x$ and wish to find x. We can rearrange the equation to give

$$(24 \cos x + 12) = (x^2 - 6)^2$$

and, writing $\cos x = y$, we find

$$\cos^{-1} y = [6 - (24y + 12)^{\frac{1}{2}}]^{\frac{1}{2}}.$$

This can be evaluated using one entry of y if we have a square root key. However, we must work out the square root of $24y + 12$ first, subtract 6, and then change the sign of the answer before taking the final square root. If we try to do the calculation directly as written, we need to keep 6 in the memory while we evaluate the first square root. The formula gives $\cos^{-1}(0.9) = 0.45105$, while the result on a full scientific calculator is $\cos^{-1}(0.9) = 0.45105$ to five figures (and in radians).

4.12. Calculation of arbitrary powers

From the ideas of section 3.5 we expect that we can get the yth power of a number close to 1 by

$$(1 + x)^y = 1 + xy$$

for *any* y (not just 2, or $\frac{1}{3}$). Suppose, for example, that we want to find $(23)^{0.53}$, but do not have a scientific calculator with an $[\![x^y]\!]$ key. If we have a square root key, we use it repeatedly to bring the number down to about 1.001. Taking the square root of 23 eleven times gives 1.0015321. The simple formula then gives $(1.0015321)^{0.53} = 1.000812$. Squaring this eleven times gives $(23)^{0.53} = 5.271$ to three figures, the exact result to three figures being 5.269. Clearly this calculation is not quite as good as the others which we have devised, but is still good enough for many purposes. For various particular powers it is possible to use the square root key directly if we remember the law of exponents. Thus

$$(4.27)^{\frac{3}{4}} = [(4.27)^3]^{\frac{1}{4}}$$

so that we cube 4.27 and take its square root twice, getting 2.97044. (Our general method gives the same result to five figures for this example.) We can similarly write $(23)^{0.53}$ as $(23)^{0.03} \times (23)^{\frac{1}{2}}$ to get 5.268.

4.13. i i, it's complex numbers again!

In section 3.15 we noted that the quantity i of complex number theory behaves like an ordinary number in algebraic manipulations, except that we set i^2 equal to -1. Now, suppose we use the series for $\exp x$ but put into it ix instead of x. We get

$$\begin{aligned}
\exp(ix) &= 1 + ix + \tfrac{1}{2}(ix)^2 + \tfrac{1}{6}(ix)^3 + \ldots \\
&= (1 - \tfrac{1}{2}x^2 \ldots) + i(x - \tfrac{1}{6}x^3 \ldots) \\
&= \cos x + i \sin x
\end{aligned}$$

since we recognize the series for $\cos x$ and $\sin x$ from section 4.4. The result obtained here is one of the most fruitful ones in the simple theory of complex numbers as it is applied in engineering and physics. We give one simple example which relates to our earlier treatment of cosines. If we suppose that $\exp x$ equals e^x even for complex numbers, we get

$$\begin{aligned}
\exp(2ix) &= e^{2ix} = (\exp ix)^2 \\
&= (\cos x + i \sin x)^2 \\
&= (\cos^2 x - \sin^2 x) + i2 \cos x \sin x.
\end{aligned}$$

However, we also should have

$$\exp(2ix) = \cos 2x + i \sin 2x$$

which suggests that

$$\begin{aligned}
\cos 2x &= \cos^2 x - \sin^2 x \\
&= \cos^2 x - (1 - \cos^2 x) \\
&= 2 \cos^2 x - 1
\end{aligned}$$

and that

$$\sin 2x = 2 \cos x \sin x.$$

We recognize the 'angle doubling' formula used in the earlier calculation of cosines. By reducing the relatively complicated algebra of sines and cosines to the more simple algebra of powers of e, this kind of calculation gives a simple but powerful way of deriving results involving the trigonometric functions. (Again, see the useful things i *does*, even if we have reservations about what it *is*!)

4.14. 'Broken calculator' games

We have seen in this chapter how we can calculate functions such as $\cos x$ and e^x even on non-scientific calculators, and in Chapter 2 we saw how to calculate things such as cube roots, for which most calculators have no special key. At various points in the text we have indicated how various keys are in a sense redundant, in that we can use other keys in combination to substitute for them. One way to develop flexibility in handling the basic results and methods of mathematics is to try 'broken calculator' games, that is, to pretend that some key (or facility) of the calculator is not working, and that we have to work out something which would normally use that key. We have seen in Chapter 3 how to get a square root when the square root key is faulty (or non-existent). What if we want to find the reciprocal of a number x and cannot use the reciprocal key *or* the division key? We cannot use the key strokes $[\![1 \div x]\!]$, but it is possible to do the calculation by various means. We take $x = 24$ as our example. We can hold 24 as the K constant and multiply by a gradually increasing series of numbers, say 0.04, 0.041 and so on. Thus, we find

$24 \times 0.041 = 0.984; \quad 24 \times 0.042 = 1.008.$

This tells us that $(24)^{-1}$ is between 0.041 and 0.042, and if we work things out 'by proportion' we estimate it to be at 0.417. We can then check that $(24)^{-1}$ is between 0.0416 and 0.0417, and so on. This process will work, but is quite lengthy if we require the result to high accuracy. A more interesting approach is to try to devise an iterative method, such as we have already encountered in several previous calculations. Suppose we work out

$$x(2 - 24x)$$

with the guess $x = (24)^{-1} + h$, h being the error between $(24)^{-1}$ and x. We get

$$[(24)^{-1} + h][2 - 24(24^{-1} + h)]$$
$$= [24^{-1} + h][1 - 24h] = 24^{-1} - 24h^2.$$

Thus, if our first guess is wrong by 0.01, the result of the calculation is wrong by 0.0024, and we can use this better x again, and so on. Thus, starting at $X = 0.04$ the successive estimates for 24^{-1} are

0.04, 0.0416, 0.04166656, 0.04166666

which gives us the result of high accuracy much more quickly than the previous approach. Only one more step is needed if we start from the worse estimate 0.03.

To use the method for X^{-1} instead of $(24)^{-1}$ we use the function $x(2 - Xx)$. Since we have met the idea of a derivative in sections 3.16 and 4.3, we can apply it here. The derivative of $2x - Xx^2$ is $2 - 2Xx$, which equals zero at $x = X^{-1}$. This is, of course, what we found out above in a longer argument, and we can see that $2x - Xx^2 = X^{-1}$ at $x = X^{-1}$. If we apply this approach to the function

$$\frac{1}{2}\frac{X}{x} + \frac{1}{2}x$$

which was used in section 3.4 to find square roots, we see that it has the derivative $-\frac{1}{2}Xx^{-2} + \frac{1}{2}$, which is zero at $x = X^{\frac{1}{2}}$. Further, at $x = X^{\frac{1}{2}}$ we have

$$\frac{1}{2}\frac{X}{x} + \frac{1}{2}x = X^{\frac{1}{2}}.$$

The calculation based on this function gives us square roots using addition, division and a memory, and it is clear that the calculus gives us a quick way to construct and analyse iterative formulae. In particular it simplifies the process of 'getting rid of the h terms' which we did in a lengthier manner in section 3.4.

When using the function $\frac{1}{2}Xx^{-1} + \frac{1}{2}x$ to calculate a square root we have a practical problem. In working out the function we destroy the X value, and the only way to avoid entering it again is to make sure that *one* cycle of the process is enough to give a good square root. This will be the case if our first guess is good enough, and we can ensure this if we use the ideas of section 3.5. Suppose we want to find $(1+X)^{\frac{1}{2}}$. We know that $1+\frac{1}{2}X$ is a good estimate for small X, and can improve on this further. We set about this by working out the square

$$(1+\tfrac{1}{2}X+KX^2)(1+\tfrac{1}{2}X+KX^2)$$
$$= 1+X+(\tfrac{1}{4}+2K)X^2+KX^3+K^2X^4.$$

If X is small, the choice $K = -\frac{1}{8}$ will remove the X^2 term and give us the best approximation to $1+X$, because X^3 and X^4 will be very small. This gives us the improved estimate

$$(1+X)^{\frac{1}{2}} = 1+\tfrac{1}{2}X-\tfrac{1}{8}X^2$$
$$= -\tfrac{1}{8}[(X-2)^2-12].$$

Now, if we want, say $(28.317)^{\frac{1}{2}}$ we write it as

$$5\times\left(\frac{28.317}{25}\right)^{\frac{1}{2}} = 5(1.13268)^{\frac{1}{2}}.$$

Using the simple formula derived above to calculate the square root gives us

$$5(1.0641396) = 5.320698.$$

The original number 28.317 can be kept in the memory while this first calculation is carried out. If the calculator has a memory exchange key, to exchange 5.320698 and 28.317, one cycle of the square root iterative process can now be carried out to give 5.321372 (the accurate root is precisely this, to six places). Similar 'hybrid' methods can be used for reciprocals and other powers, and in any particular case we have to decide whether we want speedy operation or high accuracy.

4.15. Matrices

A 2×2 *matrix* (two by two matrix) is a set of four numbers written as follows:

$$\begin{pmatrix} a & b \\ c & d \end{pmatrix}$$

a, b is called the first *row* of the matrix, and a, c the first *column* (i.e., rows are horizontal, columns are vertical). Rules for the addition and multiplication of matrices are suggested by a study of the theory of simultaneous linear equations, but we do not need that background to understand the basic idea. The product of two 2×2 matrices is *defined* as

$$\begin{pmatrix} a & b \\ c & d \end{pmatrix}\begin{pmatrix} A & B \\ C & D \end{pmatrix} = \begin{pmatrix} aA+bC & aB+bB \\ cA+dC & cB+dD \end{pmatrix}$$

i.e., it involves sums of products. A simple way to remember this rule is to note that it symbolically involves multiplying 'rows by columns'. Of course, the word product as used here does not imply that the resulting quantity must be just like the product in arithmetic. For example, we have results such as $2 \times 3 = 3 \times 2$ and so on in arithmetic, but the product of two matrices sometimes depends on which one is on the left. Thus, our rules give

$$\begin{pmatrix} 1 & 2 \\ 0 & 1 \end{pmatrix}\begin{pmatrix} 1 & 1 \\ 1 & 1 \end{pmatrix} = \begin{pmatrix} 3 & 3 \\ 1 & 1 \end{pmatrix}$$

but

$$\begin{pmatrix} 1 & 1 \\ 1 & 1 \end{pmatrix}\begin{pmatrix} 1 & 2 \\ 0 & 1 \end{pmatrix} = \begin{pmatrix} 1 & 3 \\ 1 & 3 \end{pmatrix}.$$

This *non-commutativity* of the matrix product plays an important role when matrices are applied in some branches of physics (e.g., quantum mechanics).

Now, consider the product

$$\begin{pmatrix} x & y \\ -y & x \end{pmatrix}\begin{pmatrix} X & Y \\ -Y & X \end{pmatrix} = \begin{pmatrix} xX - yY & xY + Xy \\ -xY - Xy & xX - yY \end{pmatrix}.$$

The numbers appearing in the product matrix are just the real and imaginary parts of the product complex number $(x + iy)(X + iY)$, as obtained in section 3.15. Accordingly, if we think of a kind of equivalence between complex numbers and 2×2 matrices

$$\begin{pmatrix} x & y \\ -y & x \end{pmatrix} \equiv (x + iy)$$

(what a mathematician would call a mapping), we see that we can get the complex number multiplication rule from the matrix multiplication rule. This is another example of an *isomorphism* (sameness of form) between two mathematical systems; we have encountered this idea in section 3.17. What about the mysterious number i? In our matrix approach the role of i is played by

$$\begin{pmatrix} 0 & 1 \\ -1 & 0 \end{pmatrix} \equiv (0 + i)$$

which is no more 'peculiar' than any other 2×2 matrix. We find, using the matrix multiplication rule

$$\begin{pmatrix} 0 & 1 \\ -1 & 0 \end{pmatrix}\begin{pmatrix} 0 & 1 \\ -1 & 0 \end{pmatrix} = \begin{pmatrix} -1 & 0 \\ 0 & -1 \end{pmatrix}$$

(i.e., i^2 equals minus one). The matrix on the right multiplies any 2×2 matrix throughout by -1, reversing the sign of all the four elements in it, and is the matrix version of 'minus one'. Many mathematicians argue that in view of the above results it is nowadays misleading to keep the historical adjective 'imaginary', which implies that i has some special magical qualities.

The number 1 has the property that the product $1 \times y = y$ for any number y. The 2×2 matrix with a similar property is the *unit matrix*, which contains two ones and two zeros

$$\begin{pmatrix} 1 & 0 \\ 0 & 1 \end{pmatrix}\begin{pmatrix} a & b \\ c & d \end{pmatrix} = \begin{pmatrix} a & b \\ c & d \end{pmatrix}.$$

The number zero has the property that $0 + y = y$ for any number y. Addition of 2×2 matrices is defined in the 'obvious' way,

$$\begin{pmatrix} a & b \\ c & d \end{pmatrix} + \begin{pmatrix} A & B \\ C & D \end{pmatrix} = \begin{pmatrix} a+A & b+B \\ c+C & d+D \end{pmatrix}$$

and so the analogue of the number zero is the *null matrix*, with four zeros

$$\begin{pmatrix} 0 & 0 \\ 0 & 0 \end{pmatrix} + \begin{pmatrix} a & b \\ c & d \end{pmatrix} = \begin{pmatrix} a & b \\ c & d \end{pmatrix}.$$

The *reciprocal* x^{-1} of a number x has the property $xx^{-1} = 1$. Analogously, the reciprocal of a 2×2 matrix x is that matrix which, when multiplied by x, gives the unit matrix. Not every matrix has an inverse (see exercise 5), whereas every non-zero number does have an inverse in ordinary arithmetic. In ordinary arithmetic the product of two non-zero numbers is non-zero, but this does not hold in matrix theory (where 'zero' is interpreted as the null matrix). Thus, for example,

$$\begin{pmatrix} 4 & 2 \\ 2 & 1 \end{pmatrix} \begin{pmatrix} 1 & 0 \\ -2 & 0 \end{pmatrix} = \begin{pmatrix} 0 & 0 \\ 0 & 0 \end{pmatrix}.$$

It may be that some readers with previous experience of popular mathematics books will have seen i described as an *operator* which rotates vectors or lines through an angle of 90°. i *may* be so regarded, and we can see this from our matrix approach (giving us another isomorphism, or sameness of abstract form). Consider the figure below.

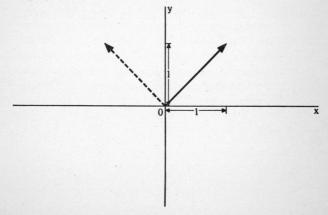

The arrow vector (the solid line) has x component equal to 1 and y component equal to 1 (i.e., we can get to the end of the arrow by moving a distance 1 east and then a distance 1 north). Now, if we put the y component and the x component into a column of two numbers and multiply it by the matrix which represents i (found previously), we find (since the second matrix has *one* column)

$$\begin{pmatrix} 0 & 1 \\ -1 & 0 \end{pmatrix}\begin{pmatrix} 1 \\ 1 \end{pmatrix} = \begin{pmatrix} 1 \\ -1 \end{pmatrix}.$$

Now, an arrow vector with y component 1 and x component -1 is the one shown as a broken line, and it is simply the original (solid line) vector rotated through 90° about the origin O. This pictorial view of i as an operator which rotates vectors through 90° holds for *any* starting vector; we chose a simple one to give a clear example. Acting twice with i obviously reverses the original vector, just as acting twice with the matrix form of i multiplies both of the elements in the column by -1.

4.16. Fahrenheit–Centigrade conversion

The conversion between temperatures in the Fahrenheit and Centigrade scales provides us with an interesting and unusual way to highlight some aspects of matrix theory. If we return to the basic matrix product rule of section 4.15, but stop half-way through forming the product we get

$$\begin{pmatrix} a & b \\ c & d \end{pmatrix}\begin{pmatrix} A \\ C \end{pmatrix} = \begin{pmatrix} aA + bC \\ cA + dC \end{pmatrix}$$

and this is defined as the product of the 2×2 matrix with the column of two elements. (We are simply using the row–column product rule for a case involving two rows and only one column.) Now consider the matrix equation

$$\begin{pmatrix} C \\ 1 \end{pmatrix} = \begin{pmatrix} \frac{5}{9} & \frac{-160}{9} \\ 0 & 1 \end{pmatrix}\begin{pmatrix} F \\ 1 \end{pmatrix}.$$

Working this out in detail gives two results:

$$C = \tfrac{5}{9}(F - 32)$$
$$1 = 1.$$

The first equation is that for the Fahrenheit–Centigrade conversion, the second is an obviously true equation (an identity). We used this peculiar way of presenting things so as to get a 2×2 matrix into the mathematics. Now, how do we get from Centigrade to Fahrenheit? From the equation involving C and F we find

$$F = \tfrac{9}{5}C + 32$$

which becomes

$$\begin{pmatrix} F \\ 1 \end{pmatrix} = \begin{pmatrix} \tfrac{9}{5} & 32 \\ 0 & 1 \end{pmatrix} \begin{pmatrix} C \\ 1 \end{pmatrix}$$

in our peculiar matrix presentation. However, using the matrix product rule we find

$$\begin{pmatrix} \tfrac{5}{9} & \tfrac{-160}{9} \\ 0 & 1 \end{pmatrix} \begin{pmatrix} \tfrac{9}{5} & 32 \\ 0 & 1 \end{pmatrix} = \begin{pmatrix} 1 & 0 \\ 0 & 1 \end{pmatrix}$$

i.e., the second 2×2 matrix is the reciprocal (or inverse) of the first 2×2 matrix. This illustrates a common feature of matrix methods: when some matrix represents a certain operation or transformation, the inverse matrix represents the inverse (or 'backwards') process which 'undoes' it.

4.17. Children's arithmetic

When small children begin to learn arithmetic they often ask their parents questions such as 'what is one and two?' If the parent answers 'three' the child says 'no, twelve!' The child is expressing what he sees, namely 1 and 2 gives 12, which he is taught to call twelve. The parent, of course, is interpreting 'and' to mean 'plus'. If we take this children's arithmetic seriously, we can actually use it to illustrate some important ideas from the theory of matrices and mappings. Suppose we use the symbol & for the 'and' process, and study only cases for which the two numbers concerned are less than ten. We can see that

$$1 \,\&\, 2 = 12 = (1 \times 10) + 2$$

or, using algebraic symbols,

$$x \ \& \ y = 10x + y$$

where $+$ is the usual addition symbol. We can quickly establish by looking at a few examples that the $\&$ operation is non-commutative, i.e., $x \ \& \ y$ and $y \ \& \ x$ are not the same. In matrix form we can set

$$(1 \ \& \ 2) = (10, 1)\binom{x}{y} = 10x + 1y$$

if a row–column product is used, or

$$\binom{1 \ \& \ 2}{0} = \begin{pmatrix} 10 & 1 \\ 0 & 0 \end{pmatrix}\binom{x}{y}$$

if we wish to use a 2×2 matrix (as in section 4.15). If we want to 'undo' the process, e.g. get from 12 to 1 & 2, we would expect that some inverse matrix would do the trick. However, we cannot find one! The 2×2 matrix involved has a zero determinant (see exercise 5) and has no inverse. We might try to find a matrix of column type such that

$$(10, 1)\binom{A}{B} = 1$$
$$= 10A + B.$$

The choice $A = X$, $B = 1 - 10X$ will satisfy this for *any* X, so we do not get a unique solution. In fact, we could set

$$\binom{1}{2} = \binom{\frac{1}{12}}{\frac{1}{6}}(12)$$

and get (1, 2) from 12, but the column with elements $\frac{1}{12}$ and $\frac{1}{6}$ would not work for another number, e.g., 23. There is no *fixed* matrix which will undo the $\&$ operation and give us x and y from $x \ \& \ y$. One way of looking at this is to say that we are trying to get two dimensions out of one dimension, which is impossible. However, our example illustrates a subtle point, which is often not appreciated. What we have found is that we cannot undo the $\&$ operation by using any fixed matrix, but this does *not* mean that the $\&$ operation cannot be undone. It can, because the reader can do it 'by eye' at once, e.g., $27 \rightarrow 2 \,\&\, 7$, $91 \rightarrow 9 \,\&\, 1$, and so on! It is expressing this process in terms of multiplications and additions by fixed numbers which is impossible, which might seem to make it difficult to instruct a calculator to do the operation for us. Some calculators can extract the integer part of a number. Starting from 12, dividing by 10 gives 1.2. Taking the integer part gives 1, and then $12 - (10 \times 1) = 2$. If we denote 'take the integer part' by T, we get the general prescription

$$x = T[(x \,\&\, y) \div 10]; \quad y = (x \,\&\, y) - (10x).$$

In fact, on an eight-figure calculator, multiplying by 10^{-9} chops off the second figure, so we get the operating rules

$$x = 10^8[10^{-9}(x \,\&\, y)]; \quad y = (x \,\&\, y) - (10x).$$

It is because the calculator is imperfect that this method works! If our conclusions above are correct, we expect that the two prescriptions above cannot be expressed in terms of 'perfect' multiplication and addition, although they can be carried out on a calculator. In particular, the rounded imperfect multiplication which a calculator performs is presumably not expressible solely in terms of 'ideal' multiplication and addition. Starting from the children's arithmetic, we have arrived at results which touch on the theory of mappings and the theory of computability. Indeed the $\&$ operation has some similarity to operations used in what is called the meta theory of logic. As often happens, exploring the questions asked by a child can lead us into deep waters!

Exercises

1. We know from the work of section 4.3, that for small h

$$\cos(x+h) = \cos x - h \sin x.$$

Suppose that for small h we have

$$\sin(x+h) = \sin x + hf$$

where f is the derivative of $\sin x$. We know that $\sin^2 + \cos^2 = 1$ both at x *and* at $x+h$. Work out this sum of squares and show that $f = \cos x$, as stated in the text.

Solution

At $x+h$, we find

$$1 = (\cos x - h\sin x)^2 + (\sin x + hf)^2$$
$$= (\cos^2 x + \sin^2 x) + 2h\sin x(f - \cos x) + h^2 \text{ terms.}$$

Since $\cos^2 x + \sin^2 x = 1$, we must have $f = \cos x$ to make the h term vanish.

2. The hyperbolic cosine, $\cosh x$, is the function defined by the equation

$$\cosh x = \tfrac{1}{2}(e^x + e^{-x}).$$

Use the exponential series to find the series for $\cosh x$, and show that for small x we can use the approximation

$$\cosh x = \tfrac{1}{24}[(x^2 + 6)^2 - 12].$$

Solution

The series is the $\exp x$ one with the odd powers omitted:

$$\cosh x = 1 + \tfrac{1}{2}x^2 + \tfrac{1}{24}x^4 + \dots$$

The odd power terms in $\exp x$ and $\exp(-x)$ cancel one another.

3. The result of the preceding problem looks like that for $\cos x$. This arises because of the relation

$$\cos x = \cosh(ix).$$

Use the ideas of section 4.4 to obtain this result, and to obtain the further result

$$\cosh 2x = 2\cosh^2 x - 1.$$

Explain how this equation can be used (by analogy with the method of section 4.4) to find $\cosh x$ for x values which are not small.

Solution

From the series for $\cosh x$ we find

$$\cosh(ix) = 1 + \tfrac{1}{2}i^2 x^2 + \tfrac{1}{24}i^4 x^4$$
$$= 1 - \tfrac{1}{2}x^2 + \tfrac{1}{24}x^4 \ldots$$
$$= \cos x \text{ (since } i^2 = -1).$$

Also, we have

$$\cosh^2 x = \tfrac{1}{4}(e^x + e^{-x})^2$$
$$= \tfrac{1}{4}(e^{2x} + e^{-2x} + 2)$$
$$= \tfrac{1}{4}(2\cosh 2x + 2)$$

whence

$$\cosh 2x = 2\cosh^2 x - 1.$$

4. If the isomorphism in section 4.15 is to work, the matrix products used must show the commutative property, because complex number products have this property. In general matrix products are not commutative; show, however, that they *are* commutative for matrices of the special form

$$\begin{pmatrix} x & y \\ -y & x \end{pmatrix}.$$

We assume here and in section 4.15 that x and y are *real* numbers. Complex number elements for matrices do appear in various parts of mathematics, but would obviously spoil our discussion here, since we want to get a model of the complex numbers starting from real numbers only.

Solution

$$\begin{pmatrix} x & y \\ -y & x \end{pmatrix}\begin{pmatrix} a & b \\ -b & a \end{pmatrix} = \begin{pmatrix} xa - yb & xb + ya \\ -ya - xb & xa - yb \end{pmatrix}$$
$$= \begin{pmatrix} a & b \\ -b & a \end{pmatrix}\begin{pmatrix} x & y \\ -y & x \end{pmatrix}.$$

5. Try to work out the numbers a, b, c, d in the matrix such that

$$\begin{pmatrix} 4 & 2 \\ 2 & 1 \end{pmatrix}\begin{pmatrix} a & b \\ c & d \end{pmatrix} = \begin{pmatrix} 1 & 0 \\ 0 & 1 \end{pmatrix}.$$

Show that b and d must satisfy conditions which are impossible, so that there cannot exist the reciprocal matrix which we are seeking. Show that if the 4 is changed to a 5 we *can* find the reciprocal matrix. This result illustrates a general rule: the matrix

$$\begin{pmatrix} a & b \\ c & d \end{pmatrix}$$

can have an inverse found for it only if the quantity $ad - bc$, called the *determinant* of the matrix, is not equal to zero. (For our example, of course, $(4 \times 1) - (2 \times 2)$ *is* zero.)

Solution

We require

$$4a + 2c = 1$$
$$4b + 2d = 0$$
$$2a + c = 0$$
$$2b + d = 1.$$

Multiplying the last equation by 2 gives $4b + 2d = 2$, but $4b + 2d = 0$ according to the second equation. It follows that no choice of b and d will work. If we have 5 instead of 4, we get

$$4b + 2d = 2$$
$$5b + 2d = 0.$$

This shows at once that $b = -2$, and thus that $d = 5$. Also we find

$$4a + 2c = 0$$
$$5a + 2c = 1$$

which gives $a = 1$, $c = 2$. We thus have the result that the reciprocal of $\begin{pmatrix} 5 & 2 \\ 2 & 1 \end{pmatrix}$ is $\begin{pmatrix} 1 & -2 \\ -2 & 5 \end{pmatrix}$.

6. In scientific work the absolute temperature scale (or Kelvin scale) is often used. The formula for converting from the Kelvin scale to the Centigrade scale is

$$C = K - 273.$$

Write this in a way which involves a 2×2 matrix, as in section 4.15.

Find the formula which converts from the Kelvin scale to the Fahrenheit scale, and write this in the matrix form also. Show that the 2×2 matrix for this Kelvin to Fahrenheit conversion is the *product* of the matrices for the Kelvin to Centigrade and Centigrade to Fahrenheit conversions.

Solution

$$\begin{pmatrix} C \\ 1 \end{pmatrix} = \begin{pmatrix} 1 & -273 \\ 0 & 1 \end{pmatrix} \begin{pmatrix} K \\ 1 \end{pmatrix} \qquad (K \to C)$$

$$\begin{pmatrix} F \\ 1 \end{pmatrix} = \begin{pmatrix} 1.8 & 32 \\ 0 & 1 \end{pmatrix} \begin{pmatrix} C \\ 1 \end{pmatrix} \qquad (C \to F)$$

$$= \begin{pmatrix} 1.8 & 32 \\ 0 & 1 \end{pmatrix} \begin{pmatrix} 1 & -273 \\ 0 & 1 \end{pmatrix} \begin{pmatrix} K \\ 1 \end{pmatrix}$$

$$= \begin{pmatrix} 1.8 & -459.4 \\ 0 & 1 \end{pmatrix} \begin{pmatrix} K \\ 1 \end{pmatrix} \qquad (K \to F)$$

7. A hill has a gradient of 1 in 10. What angle (in degrees) does the road make to the horizontal?

Solution

'1 in 10' usually means a rise of 1 foot for each 10 feet moved.

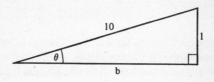

Accordingly, $10^2 = 100 = 1 + b^2$

$$\cos \theta = \frac{b}{10} = \frac{\sqrt{99}}{10} = \sqrt{0.99}.$$

Now $\sqrt{(1-h)} = 1 - \frac{1}{2}h$ for small h, so we have the result $\sqrt{0.99} \simeq 0.995$. (A calculator gives 0.9949874 for this square root.)

The formula of section 3.7,

$$\cos^{-1} y = [6 - (24y + 12)^{\frac{1}{2}}]^{\frac{1}{2}}$$

gives $\cos^{-1}y = 0.10004$ radian at $y = 0.995$. (This angle is 5.732 degrees; the exact result is actually 5.739 degrees.)

8. Consider a rectangle with sides of length x and y, so that the perimeter equals $2(x+y)$ and the area equals xy. Suppose that the perimeter is fixed at 10 cm, but x is variable. What is the biggest area which can be obtained, and what x value gives it? Do the calculation numerically, and also by using the idea of a derivative.

Solution

$$10 = 2(x+y)$$
$$\text{Thus} \quad y = 5-x$$
$$\text{Area} = xy = (5-x)x = 5x - x^2$$
$$\text{Derivative} = 5 - 2x = 0 \text{ if } x = 2.5$$
$$\text{Maximum area} = (2.5)^2 = 6.25.$$

We find that a square has the maximum area for a given fixed perimeter.

9. A metal rod of length 10.0320 cm expands to length 10.0336 if heated from 20°C to 100°C. What is the coefficient of expansion of the metal?

Solution

The expansion coefficient is the fractional change in length per one degree rise in temperature. Strictly speaking, the coefficient changes slightly with temperature, but this can be ignored for many problems. We find

$$\frac{10.0336 - 10.0320}{(100 - 20)} = 0.00002.$$

10. According to a statement in the House of Commons, between February 1974 and February 1978 the value of a pound declined to 53 pence. What does that mean, and what average annual percentage decline of the pound is involved? What average annual rate of inflation is involved?

Solution

A pound had in 1978 the same purchasing power as 53 pence had in 1974. If the purchasing power declines a fractional rate r per annum, we have

$$(1-r)^4 = 0.53.$$

Thus $r = 1-(0.53)^{\frac{1}{4}}$
$$= 0.147 \ (15\%).$$

(To find the fourth root we press the square root key twice.)

Inflation is measured in terms of the prices of goods. In the four years prices have gone up in the ratio 1 to 0.53, i.e., 1.8868 to 1. The average annual inflation rate is f, where $1.8868 = (1+f)^4$. This gives $f = 0.1720 \ (17\%)$. (Politicians may note that the first way of describing the facts gives the smaller number!)

11. The definition of the natural log, ln, is, as stated in section 4.6:

If $\qquad \exp x = y$
then $\qquad x = \ln y$ (log to base e of y).

(logs to base 10 were treated in section 2 of Chapter 1). We can also condense this information into a single equation,

$$\exp(\ln x) = x.$$

Suppose now that $y = \ln(1+x)$, so that

$$\exp y = 1+x.$$

If y changes slightly, to $y+h$, then x will also change, to $x+H$, say. Can you find the ratio (h/H), which will give us the derivative of $\ln(1+x)$ with respect to x?

Solution

$$\exp(y+h) = \exp y + h\exp y$$

from the known properties of $\exp x$ (section 4.6), with h very small. However,

$$\exp(y+h) = 1+x+H$$

by definition. Since $\exp y = 1 + x$, we find from these two equations that

$$H = h \exp y = h(1+x).$$

Thus,

$$\frac{h}{H} = \frac{1}{(1+x)}.$$

Thus, if $y = \ln(1+x)$, and x changes by a small amount, y changes by an amount $(1+x)^{-1}$ times as great, i.e., the derivative of $\ln(1+x)$ is $(1+x)^{-1}$. The reason why $\ln(1+x)$ is usually studied instead of $\ln x$ is that setting $x = 0$ in $\ln(1+x)$ gives $\ln 1$, which is zero, while setting $x = 0$ in $\ln x$ gives $-\infty$ (minus infinity).

12. Modify the method used in section 4.9 (for logs to base 2) to give logs to base 10 and find $\log_{10} 3$ on a simple calculator.

Solution

The prescription is as in the text, except for the change of the number 2 wherever it appears to the number 10. The list of recorded numbers is

0111101000100...

and this leads to the result $\log_{10} 3 = 0.4771$ (to four places).

13. If all 26 letters of the English alphabet are equally likely to occur in a long passage of text, what is the information content I per letter? Is I increased or decreased if the letters are not equally probable?

Solution

There are 26 possibilities, each with probability $\frac{1}{26}$. The sum is thus

$$I = -26 \times (\tfrac{1}{26} \log_2 \tfrac{1}{26})$$
$$= \log_2 26$$

since $\log(\frac{1}{x}) = -\log x$ (for any base)
$\log_2 (26)$ is 4.76, so we have $I = 4.76$ bits per letter.

Of course, all letters are *not* equally probable. J. R. Pierce, in his book *Symbols, Signals and Noise*, gives a readable account of studies on the relative frequency of appearance of the different letters. If some letters hardly ever appear, we are *less* uncertain about what a symbol can be, and I decreases. If, for example, only two letters appeared most of the time, we would be back to $I = 1$ bit. Written English actually has $I \simeq 2.14$ bits per letter, when allowance is made for the different probabilities of occurrence of letters, pairs of letters, triples of letters etc.

14. According to theory the specific heat c of a metal at low temperatures should vary with the absolute temperature t according to the law

$$c = at + bt^3$$

where a and b are constants. How could we plot a graph to give a straight line if this law is true (i.e., what should we use as the two variables to plot on the graph)?

Solution

Plot ct^{-1} versus t^2. We have

$$\frac{c}{t} = a + bt^2$$

and so would get a straight line with slope b and intercept a.

15. If the air in a sealed cylinder, such as that of a bicycle pump, is suddenly compressed so that it heats up, the relationship between the volume v of the air and the absolute temperature t of the air is that t is proportional to $v^{-0.4}$. (This is the adiabatic expansion law from simple physics.) The pressure p of the gas will be proportional to $v^{-(1.4)}$. Suppose the gas starts at $t = 300$ and $p = 1$ atmosphere. What pressure (in atmospheres) is needed to decrease the volume by 30% and what is the air temperature produced?

Solution

To get a 0.4 power we can use either a scientific calculator or the method of section 4.12; the volume *ratio* is 0.7, so the t *ratio* is $(0.7)^{-0.4} = (1.4285714)^{0.4}$ and the p *ratio* is $(0.7)^{-1.4} =$

$(1.4285714)^{1.4}$. These ratios work out to be 1.153 and 1.648, respectively.

16. If the pressure in a sound wave at some test frequency has to increase by 9% before the sound increase can just be discerned, by how many decibels must the sound increase before the change is noticed? What percentage of judged sound intensity does the increase represent?

Solution

The pressure ratio is 1.09, so the decibel increase is given by

$$20\log_{10}(1.09) = 0.75,$$

i.e., the smallest discernible increase has a constant value (about $\frac{3}{4}$) in decibel units. This is usually what people mean when they loosely say that 'hearing obeys a logarithmic scale'. If the judged sound intensity varies as $(pressure)^{0.3}$, a 9% increase in pressure represents an increase of 2.6% in judged sound intensity:

$$[\![1.09 \ X^y \ 0.3 \ =]\!] \quad \boxed{1.0261904}.$$

This result might appear peculiar, but if we think of the relationship between judged intensity and pressure as set out on a graph (as in section 4.8), then the points are the actual observed results, although we can fit them to a mathematical line which 'fills in the gaps' and gives the false impression that we can move along it in as small jumps as we please.

17. If two separate sound sources of equal strength are heard together, is the number of decibels doubled?

Solution

No. If the two sound waves have no special relationship with one another, the rule is that the *powers* in the two waves are added. Thus the formula to use is

$$\text{Decibels} = 10 \times \log_{10} \text{ (power ratio)}$$
$$= 10 \times \log_{10}(2) = 3.01.$$

For example, 70 decibels plus 70 decibels gives 73 decibels. This is the same result as would have been obtained by doubling the power output of a single source. If the two waves have the same frequency and can be aligned so that the pressure peaks of one wave coincide with the pressure troughs of the other wave, the resultant sound is weakened by destructive interference. This 'adding of sound to get silence' can be done under controlled laboratory conditions, and research has been done which shows that it is possible to set up 'counter-sound' which will largely cancel the noise produced by rotating-shaft machinery, even when the sound contains a spread of frequencies.

18. Suppose that by the method of section 4.12 we find $(2.312)^{\frac{1}{3}}$ = 1.322. Show how to get a more accurate result quickly by using $(1+x)^{\frac{1}{3}} \simeq 1+\frac{1}{3}x = \frac{1}{3}(2+1+x)$.

Solution

We work out $2.312 \div (1.322)^3 = \boxed{1.0006758}$.

Key strokes $[\![+\ \ 2\ \ \div\ \ 3]\!]$ then give $\boxed{1.0002252}$.

$1.0002252 \times 1.322 = 1.3222977$.

Chapter 5
How the Calculator Works

5.1. Chips and all that

The tiny silicon chip is the most important part of the calculator. Silicon is the material almost universally used, because it makes good transistor material and also has an oxide which is a good insulator. A thin silicon wafer, sliced from a long cylindrical crystal, can produce many chips (side by side on the area of the wafer). The basic construction process involves the formation of regions of *n* and *p* type by diffusing atoms of other elements into the surface of the silicon. An *n* type region is one containing an impurity such as phosphorus, which, when it is imbedded in the silicon lattice, releases extra electrons which can carry an electric current. A *p* type region is one containing an impurity such as boron, which in effect tries to *reduce* the number of electrons available to carry current. The effect of this reduction, however, is that the *p* type material conducts by means of 'holes', which behave like electrons with a positive charge instead of a negative one. The theory of this behaviour has been known for a long time to solid state physicists, and transistors with *n* and *p* regions have been widely employed in radio and television engineering. The new 'microelectronic revolution' is due to the ability to pack thousands of tiny transistors together on the surface of the tiny silicon chip. In cheap calculators the impurity boron is widely used, giving electrical conduction by holes in the tiny transistor units. Holes move more slowly than electrons in most materials, so the operating speed of chips is not as high if they use hole current carriers; nevertheless, the speed is still incredibly fast as far as the human operator is concerned! A lengthy explanation of the use of photo-resist layers and optical masks to map out the impurity regions in the silicon surface is given in a book published by Scientific American entitled *Microelectronics*. Here we briefly indicate schematically the layout of the most common transistor type used in calculators. A MOSFET (metal oxide semiconductor field effect transistor) is based on a layout as shown below (thousands of these being set out side by side on a chip):

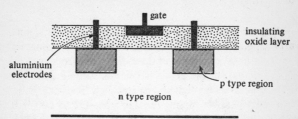

When the two *p* type regions are connected to a voltage source no current can flow between them unless the central electrode (the gate) has a negative pulse applied to it. The pulse repels the excess electrons of the *n* type barrier away from a thin layer at the top of the *n* type region and produces a hole conduction path between the two *p* type regions. Clearly the speed at which this turning-on can occur depends on the mobility of the current carriers and also on the thickness of the oxide layer under the gate electrode. Depending on its detailed design, a calculator chip may operate with positive or negative voltage pulses (or both); by changing over *n* and *p* type regions in the above diagram we get a transistor which is turned on by a positive pulse and is turned off by a zero pulse. To do binary arithmetic all we need is a pair of standard signals which represent 1 and 0 in binary code. The transistors (unlike those in a radio) are mainly used as on–off switches. It has recently been suggested that materials such as gallium arsenide (at present used for L.E.D. displays – see p. 29) may be of use as transistor materials, since they would lead to current carriers (holes and electrons) with high mobility. Whether the consequent higher calculating speeds could be obtained without excessive cost and chip design problems remains to be seen.

5.2. Binary addition

Consider the sum $5+3 = 8$; if we translate into binary code this becomes

5	101
+3	11
= 8	1000

In adding the units column we get $1+1$, which is 2 or '0 units plus 1 carry', and so on. In each column except the units one, we have to be ready to take an input of three digits, one from each number and one carry from the previous column. Adding these three we get an output of a sum digit and a carry digit. Thus at each column we get eight possible inputs, ranging from 111 to 000, and four possible outputs, ranging from 11 to 00. A circuit to perform the addition can be formed using only various interconnections of simple logical NAND gates, so arranged that they produce the correct input–output characteristics. A NAND ('not and') gate will give a positive output pulse (binary 1) unless *all* the inputs have a positive pulse (binary 1), when it will give a zero output pulse (binary 0). A single-input NAND gate will simply act as a negation or NOT gate, changing 0 to 1 and 1 to 0. To form a two-input NAND gate, for example, requires two MOSFET transistors and a resistor in series:

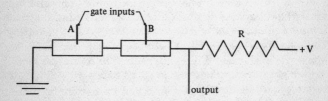

When *both* inputs A and B receive a positive pulse, both transistors are turned on; the current flow produces a voltage drop across resistance R, so that output C drops almost to earth potential. If the pulses are not both positive at A and B, the output at C is $+V$ volts. The input pairs (10), (01), (00) give output 1, while input (11) gives output 0. Passing the output from C into a single-input NAND gate then reverses it, and gives us the correct carry digit needed for the addition of two binary digit inputs at A and B. To construct a full adder circuit, with three inputs per unit, capable of dealing with a long binary number, requires the interconnection of hundreds of NAND units, but the point about modern micro-electronics is that such large numbers of transistors can be packed into a small area on one silicon chip.

There is one feature of the description above which must be puzzling to the reader who knows some electrical circuit theory: if we contrive to put in varying inputs at *A* and *B*, but never put them both positive together, we get a constant 1 output. How does this continuous permanent 1 get interpreted as, say, 1 or 11 or 111 in a binary code made up of *separate* binary digits? The answer is that calculators, and electronic computers in general, have an electronic oscillator or *clock* which defines the length of each digit and controls the rate of progress of the pulses through each part of the circuitry. In effect, then, the output at *C* would be sampled at regular intervals, coinciding with the input pulses at *A* and *B*, and the permanent 1 would come out as a string of binary 1s. The clock frequency is typically tens of thousands of cycles per second, so that an addition of two numbers, even if it takes hundreds of cycles, appears to take place instantaneously. The limitation on speed for a simple calculator is provided by the speed at which the human operator can key in the numbers; this is why throughout this book we emphasize key sequences which reduce the number of key strokes to perform calculations.

5.3. Subtraction. Complements

Consider the subtraction $1082 - 293$, in base 10. Most readers will probably do this mentally as follows,

$$(1082 - 300) + 7 = 782 + 7 = 789.$$

This splits the calculation up into a very simple operation involving hundreds and an addition operation. In a similar spirit it is possible to make the subtraction of binary numbers look like addition if we introduce the *complement* $\bar{x}$ of a binary number x. $\bar{x}$ is obtained simply by changing 1 to 0 and 0 to 1 within the number x. Here is an example in which a four-digit number is added to its complement (with the base 10 translation being given to make the calculation shorter):

x	1010	10
$\bar{x}$	0101	5
	1111	15

Now, if we change x by converting, say, a 0 to a 1, then $\bar{x}$ will have a 1 changed to a 0, and the sum $x + \bar{x}$ will *still* be 15. We note that $15 = 2^4 - 1$, and by inspecting a few more cases (or by a little algebra!) we obtain the result

$$x + \bar{x} = 2^n - 1 \quad \text{(for } n \text{ digit numbers).}$$

If we want to do a subtraction $y - x$, then, we can do it as follows:

$$\begin{aligned} y - x &= y + \bar{x} - (x + \bar{x}) \\ &= y + \bar{x} + 1 - 2^n. \end{aligned}$$

For example,

	Subtraction			Addition	
y	1101	(13)	y	1101	(13)
x	1010	(10)	$\bar{x}$	0101	(5)
			1	1	(1)
	0011	(3)		10011	(19)

To find $y - x$ we form the sum $y + \bar{x} + 1$ and delete the 1 at the left-hand end of the result. Subtraction has thus been reduced to addition, together with simple operations which a binary arithmetic unit can do easily.

5.4. Multiplication. Shifts

To multiply two numbers in base 10 we write down rows for units, tens, etc. and add them. We can proceed similarly in binary code. For example:

Base ten		*Base two*	
	24		11000
×	11	×	1011
	24		11000
	240		110000
			11000000
	264		
			100001000

The binary calculation involves the addition of several binary numbers, each one being derived from the preceding one by a simple shift to the left. Thus this simple shift operation together with binary addition serve to perform binary multiplication. Binary division can be converted to repeated shift and subtraction; by considering the multiplication given above, we see that to divide a binary number x by a binary number y we form various shifted versions of y. There will be a largest one, y_1, which gives a positive $x - y_1$, another largest one y_2 which makes $(x - y_1) - y_2$ positive, etc.; by keeping track of the numbers y_1, y_2, etc., used we can construct the binary number for $264 \div 24$.

5.5. Binary coded decimals

The preceding sections have indicated briefly how the four basic operations of arithmetic can be reduced to addition and a few other simple operations for binary numbers. Addition in turn can be performed by simple combinations of NAND and other units which are formed out of the basic MOSFET transistors in the silicon chip. Most calculators operate on a variation of the binary system called the binary coded decimal system. In that system a number such as 15 (fifteen) is regarded as 'one-five' and written as 0001 0101. Each decimal digit is written as a separate four-digit binary number. Using four digits we can represent binary numbers up to 15, but only need to represent digits up to 9. The left-over binary symbols can be used for other machine instructions such as $\pm$, $\times$, etc., so that both instructions and data are used in binary form in the calculator. The principles involved in doing arithmetic in BCD form are basically the same as for binary arithmetic, but the details of the algorithm must be modified. L. Nashelsky's book *Digital Computer Theory* describes several alternative codes, one being the excess three code, in which the binary number 0011 is added to each digit in the BCD code. This simple change has a useful effect, as we illustrate by looking at the addition $8 + 7 = 15$:

Binary	Excess three
1000	1011
0111	1010
----	-----
1111	10101

1111 is *not* a BCD symbol for a number, while 10101 is the BCD form for 15 (if we omit the leading zeros). Thus adding the excess three version of the numbers gives the correct BCD form of the result in this case. A given machine will use one particular code, not a mixed one as we did here. If we stick to the BCD form we can obtain the result by adding 6 (i.e., 0110) to the ordinary binary sum, which gives 10101 in our example. Alternatively, in excess three code we add 0011 to each digit of the excess three sum. The extra addition is done automatically by the calculator and is *only* needed when one of the four-digit components in the sum exceeds 0101, corresponding to a 'carry' in the decimal form of the addition. For example, to add 2 to 3 in BCD we can proceed with no use of the extra 6; the calculator spots this automatically and brings in the 6 when necessary. The reason why the 6 'does the trick' is that to produce a 1 in the fifth column of the binary number requires $2^4 = 16$, whereas to get a decimal 'carry' we need 10 (ten). Adding 6 thus converts the decimal carry correctly into a BCD carry. Since multiplication is simply repeated addition, it can be done in BCD if 6 is added to convert to BCD any number which is too big. For instance, consider the case $7 \times 3 = 21$:

Binary		BCD	
111		0111	
11		0011	
0111		0111	
1110	add 6 →	10100	
10101		11011	add 6 → 10 0001 (21)

BCD arithmetic is only slightly more complicated than ordinary binary arithmetic, but the BCD system is clearly easier when it comes to the input or output (display) of decimal numbers, since each set of four binary digits gives a definite decimal digit. If we key in the number 23, for example, we first press 2, then 3. The calculator does not know that we shall press anything after the 2 key, and we can compare the binary and BCD forms of the numbers as follows:

	Binary	BCD	
2	10	0010	
23	10111	0010	0011

It is clearly easier to put the digits in and move the previous ones along in BCD than to make the complicated change in the number which would arise if we stuck to the simple binary code. Indeed, by using the plus 6 rule explained above, we are really getting as close as possible to doing decimal arithmetic at all stages, while still using only binary digits which are suited to the simple 'on–off' properties of the transistors in the calculator chip.

5.6. General operating features

It is clear that to perform a sum such as $3 + 2 = 5$ the calculator must have a store for the 3, another for the 2, and another for the + instruction. It also must have some pre-recorded instructions to carry out the addition operation when the $[\![=]\!]$ key is pressed, and also a decoder unit to put the input numbers and display numbers into BCD and decimal form, respectively. The stores for the numbers 3 and 2 are usually called the x and y registers, and the store for the operation ($+$, $\times$, etc.) is called the flag register. Some calculators (e.g., the CBM 899D) have a key marked $[\![x-y]\!]$, which will exchange the contents of the x and y registers; thus, the key strokes below give the results shown:

$$[\![3 \div 2 =]\!] \quad \boxed{1.5}$$
$$[\![3 \div 2 \ x-y =]\!] \quad \boxed{0.666}$$

showing that the $x-y$ operation has exchanged the numerator and denominator in the division. The following interesting sequence is also obtained:

$$[\![3 \div x-y]\!] \quad \boxed{3}.$$

This indicates that as $[\![\div]\!]$ is pressed, showing that the first number is completed, the first number fills up the other register, and is later cleaned out of the first register by the second input number. This ensures that if the keys $[\![3 \times =]\!]$ are pressed, the x and y registers *both* contain 3 and the result is $3 \times 3 = 9$, the automatic K constant operation. The automatic K constant operation is thus achieved by this simple rule for passing the input through the x and y registers in turn. When the $[\![=]\!]$ key is pressed the operation in the flag register brings into play the appropriate set of instructions from the ROM (read-only memory), and these instructions pass the contents of the x and y registers through the arithmetic unit, where the appropriate calculation is performed. The result is then put in another store, the results register, and also copied into the x and y registers in case it is needed in a continuing calculation such as $3+2\times5$. The results register feeds the display. In the case of a scientific calculator or programmable calculator it may be that many intermediate results are formed in a long calculation, with only the last one being displayed. The results register might then be isolated from the display until the calculation is completed. Some calculators do not have this feature (e.g., the Prinztronic Program and some Hewlett-Packard machines), but most algebraic logic calculators (which we are describing here) do have it.

Those registers which can be controlled by the operator are made up of tiny units consisting of a capacitor and a switching transistor which connects it to the other circuitry. Each unit stores a binary 1 or 0 (i.e., the condenser is either charged or uncharged). In the case of the permanent read-only memory this elaboration is not necessary – the condenser can be replaced either by a permanent open circuit or short circuit to represent 1 or 0. By making the ROM out of many units with fusible links, an appropriate set of binary digits can be permanently stored by passing a pattern of current pulses through the ROM to burn out some of the fuses. This leaves a pattern of open (fused) and closed (unfused) elements. Scanning portions of the ROM, at a rate determined by the basic clock frequency, will produce the recorded sequence of binary digits.

The keyboard is also scanned at high frequency. Horizontal 'scan lines' (rows of keys) are activated in turn. If a key is pressed, a signal will come out along the appropriate 'input line' (i.e., vertical column of keys). The pressed key is thus specified as being, say, 'third row, second column', and produces a predetermined BCD signal from the encoder circuitry. The display itself is pulsed at high frequency, and in some calculators may be drawing energy from the battery for about a tenth of the time during which it is displaying a number. Many calculator displays look like a row of 8s when the calculator is turned off; close inspection reveals that each digit is formed by 7 small segments which form an 8 shape. By lighting up some selection of these 7 segments any number from 0 to 9 can be made to appear. The usual red light-emitting diodes employ the semi-conductor gallium arsenide, and the display digits for L.E.D. displays are usually magnified by tiny cylindrical lenses. Green digitron displays also use electrical power to emit light. On the other hand liquid crystal displays use much less power; much work on biphenyl liquid crystal displays has been done in the Chemistry Department at the University of Hull. The electrical input to a liquid crystal display alters the light transmission properties of the segments in the digits, so that the contrast of the segments against a background is changed. No power is used to actually generate light, so power consumption is low. Visibility of the display is also good, except in complete darkness! One trick which seems to help with simple calculators is to clear numbers by entering new numbers (or zero); when the battery is low this procedure does not stop the calculator, whereas pressing the clear key often *does* do so.

5.7. Algorithms

All calculators have a set of instructions in their R O M which will carry out the four operations $+$, $-$, $\times$, $\div$ of ordinary arithmetic. Many calculators have keys for $\sqrt{\ }$, and scientific calculators have keys for $\cos x$, e^x, etc. All these extra functions are worked out using built-in programs which mainly use the four basic operations. For example, a square root could be worked out using an iterative process such as that of section 3.4, and some calculators probably do it that way. The details of the algorithms are kept secret by most manufacturers, although the square root algorithm used in a simple Casio calculator has been described by D. R. Green and J. Lewis, in their book *Science with Pocket Calculators*. To a human operator the algorithm looks very laborious, as do most of the available algorithms, but the calculator can do the vast number of operations needed in a fraction of a second. In the *Hewlett-Packard Journal* there appear from time to time accounts of some of the algorithms used on H P calculators. (These are reverse Polish calculators, but A.O.S. algorithms could perform similar tasks.) The *I B M Journal* has also published material on calculator algorithms, in particular on the 'pseudo-division' processes which feature prominently in H P calculator algorithms. We give two examples to illustrate the idea. To find $\ln x$, the number x is repeatedly divided by 2, 1.1, 1.01, etc., until it is expressed in the form

$$x = 2^a(1.1)^b(1.01)^c(1.001)^d \ldots$$

a, b, c, d, etc., are integers, and the natural log of x is constructed as a sum

$$\ln x = a \ln 2 + b \ln 1.1 + c \ln 1.01 + \ldots$$

The values of $\ln 2$, $\ln 1.1$, etc., are kept as stored constants in the machine. The algorithm which we gave in section 4.9 for logs to any base also uses this 'breaking-up' (pseudo-division) kind of process, but has the advantage of not needing any peculiar constants. (Whether it would be useful in a calculator is an interesting question; it may already have been secretly tried!) When dealing with functions such as $\cos x$, $\sin x$, $\tan x$, the pseudo-division approach is to break up x into a sum of specified numbers:

$$x = an_1 + bn_2 + cn_3 + \ldots$$

Here the numbers n_1, n_2 etc. are stored constants, with the property

$$\tan n_1 = 1, \quad \tan n_2 = 0.1, \quad \tan n_3 = 0.01, \text{ etc.}$$

Tan x can then be constructed by building up the angle from its component parts. The actual procedure of this building up appears to be a little complicated in the HP system, but in principle it is equivalent to the use of the basic formula for $\tan(x+y)$:

$$\tan(x+y) = \frac{\tan x + \tan y}{1 - \tan x \tan y}$$

with the simplification that tan y is always some simple negative power of 10. Cos x and sin x can be calculated from $\tan \frac{1}{2}x$, so the procedure in various calculators is to work out $\tan \frac{1}{2}x$ first by some algorithm and then derive the other two functions from it if required. Thus a tan is worked out internally even if the cos x key is pressed. In our simple algorithms of section 4.4 we took the cos x function as the one to be the basic one, because of the simple algorithm which it involves. Whether any of the calculator algorithms in use follow this route is not known to the author; our algorithms were constructed so as to be simple for a human operator, whereas calculator algorithms are not subject to this constraint.

Exercises

1. Suppose that the 'complements addition' process of section 5.3 is used to subtract two four-digit binary numbers, but that no 1 results in the left row, where the 2^4 should be (before being chopped off). What does this mean? (Assume that it doesn't just mean that we can't add up properly!)

Solution

The missing 1 means that we have a negative number. Thus, if we work out 12–10 in binary we get 10010 if we follow the rules, whereas if we work out 10–12 we get 1110. This looks like 14, but is supposed to be -2. It is *still* 2^4 greater than the true answer, of course, but the extra 2^4 is not just represented by a 1 stuck on the left-hand end. In a calculator, it is easy to arrange for subtractions to give positive answers, by swopping the numbers over and sticking a minus sign on to the answer. This removes the problem. An alternative but more complicated procedure is to change the rules, as follows. To find $x - y$ we add x to $\bar{y}$ (with *no* extra 1). If the 1 appears on the left we drop it and add 1 to the rest of the answer (which gives us what we would have got under the previous rules). If there is no extra 1 on the left we form the complement of the answer and prefix a negative sign.

Thus 10–12 becomes

10	1010
$\overline{12}$	0011
Add	1101 → -0010 → -2

2. How can we get $\sin x$ and $\cos x$ if we know $\tan \frac{1}{2}x$? Would it be sufficient just to know $\tan x$?

Solution

By manipulating the formulae

$$\cos 2x = 2\cos^2 x - 1$$

and

$$\cos^2 x + \sin^2 x = 1$$

we can obtain the 'tan half angle formulae',

$$\cos x = \frac{1 - t^2}{1 + t^2}; \ \sin x = \frac{2t}{1 + t^2}$$

where $t = \tan \frac{1}{2}x$. We also have, of course,

$$\tan x = \frac{2t}{1 - t^2}$$

and the formulae above give the *correct sign* for the three functions. If we use a formula such as, say,

$$\cos^2 x(1 + \tan^2 x) = 1$$

to get $\cos x$ from $\tan x$, we must get the sign of $\cos x$ right by noting whether x is less than $\pi/2$, etc. This extra decision making is easy if the x value is small, but would involve a lengthy decision procedure for large x values.

Chapter 6
Programmable Calculators

6.1. Introduction

This last chapter deals briefly with programmable calculators. Only a few of these calculators can be called pocket calculators, because of their size, and also because they do not give very long battery life when used 'in the field'. Since low battery power leads to erroneous results or to fade-out of the display, the present author has found that long programmed calculations are best done with a mains unit as the power supply. At the time of writing (April 1978) two of the most powerful programmable calculators are the Hewlett-Packard HP29-C and the Texas Instruments T.I.58. A comparison test of these machines was reported in the December 1977 issue of the calculator journal *Keyboard*. The HP29-C uses reverse Polish logic (see section 1.3), while the T.I.58 uses A.O.S. algebraic logic (see section 1.2). In the somewhat lower price range there are, for example, the Casio fx201P calculator, the T.I.57 (a lower-powered version of the T.I.58) and the Sinclair Cambridge Programmable. This last one genuinely *is* a small pocket calculator; although it only has thirty-six steps in its program length, it does have a jump facility (see section 6.2).

Programmable calculators are effectively low-powered computers; there are various scientific and professional jobs for which it may be less expensive and more convenient to carry out small-scale calculations on a calculator rather than on a full-scale computer. In school use a programmable calculator could well be collectively owned by the school and used to demonstrate mathematical calculations in scientific or mathematics classes (and also to do calculations connected with administration!).

6.2. Jump instructions

Each calculator has a stated number of program steps which it can remember and execute on request. Accordingly, if our calculation needs more steps than the calculator can store, it might seem that we are defeated. Suppose, for example, that we need 110 steps and the machine stores only 100 steps. The clever thing to do is to re-design the mathematics so that the calculation can be done more briefly. If polynomials are being calculated the kind of tricks described in sections 2.1 and 2.6 may be useful. If this does not 'shrink' the program sufficiently, it is possible to do the last few steps manually. The steps are carefully written out on paper as though the calculator *could* do them, but it is only programmed up to 100 steps. The last ten steps are then done manually by the operator, starting from the data left in the machine at the end of the first 100 steps. Alternatively, the operator can do his ten steps first and let the machine finish off, if he writes the program appropriately. This latter procedure is useful for calculators which take up some steps in putting in the data. For example, on the Casio fx201P, to put starting data into the stores 1 to 5 should involve a program instruction with eleven steps:

$[\![ENT\ 1 : 2 : 3 : 4 : 5 :]\!]$.

However, to save eight steps we can put the data manually into stores 2 to 5, and start the program off by only 'officially' filling store 1, i.e., using $[\![ENT\ 1 :]\!]$. The calculator acts on what it finds in the stores, no matter how it got there. (This can cause problems if we accidentally leave something from a previous calculation!)

In Chapters 2 and 3 we came across iterative processes, which simply go round and round the same cycle of calculations. Here is an ideal way to beat the limitation on the number of steps in the program. If the calculation can be made into an iterative one, a basic cycle of, say, eighty steps, could lead to a calculation of any length, provided that we can join the 'tail to the nose'. (For example, you can run a ten-mile race on a running circuit of any size!) It is this joining process which is vital, and it is accomplished by $[\![JUMP]\!]$ or $[\![GO\ TO]\!]$ type instructions. A programmable calculator which can have a jump as one of its program steps really escapes from the limitation of finite program memory and becomes a mini-computer. To add a jump facility amounts to a qualitative change in the nature of the machine, and most modern machines have this facility (all the machines mentioned in the introduction do so). Of course, a simple jump is not of great use, since it would usually make the machine run for ever. If we told the calculator at step 100 to jump back to step 50, say, and keep going, we should find that the calculator would go through the steps $1 \rightarrow 50 \rightarrow 100 \rightarrow 50 \rightarrow 100$ and so on, ad infinitum! What we need is some kind of *conditional* jump which makes the calculator jump back to step 50 only if some number (in one of the stores) has not exceeded some specified limit. As an example, to get just ten 'loops' performed, we could put into the program (after step 50) a part which adds 1 to the contents of store 7. At step 100 we could have an instruction of type: jump to step 50 if the number in store 7 is less than 10. If we put zero in store 7 at step 1, the calculator will go round the $(50 \rightarrow 100)$ loop ten times and stop at step 100. This is a simple example, and many modern machines can perform more complicated jumps (e.g., jump if the number in store 7 is greater than the number in store 6). Anyone intending to do serious scientific calculating, then, should pay careful attention to the jump facilities on any calculator which he intends to purchase.

6.3. The use of labelled memories

All programmable calculators have a set of memories or stores, with numbers as labels; the program moves numbers into and out of these stores and does various calculations with them. The basic principle to remember is that a number which has been recalled from a store into the central arithmetic unit will be treated just as would a number which the operator had keyed in manually. There is not much point in giving here lengthy pieces of program which refer only to one particular calculator. We shall show some typical features of currently available machines by looking at one little problem: we wish to multiply together the numbers in stores 3 and 2, add the number in store 1 to the result, then add 3, and put the final result in store 4. Some current machines and their program segments for this are as follows (the Sinclair Enterprise steps are the same as the T.I.58 ones, except that $[\![RCL]\!]$ becomes the two-stroke sequence $[\![\varDelta \ RCL]\!]$):

Casio fx201P $[\![4 = 3 \times 2 + 1 + K3 :]\!]$
Texas Instruments T.I.58
$\qquad [\![RCL\ 3 \times RCL\ 2 + RCL\ 1 + 3 = STO\ 4]\!]$
Hewlett-Packard HP29-C
$\qquad [\![RCL\ 3\ RCL\ 2 \times RCL\ 1 + 3 + STO\ 4]\!]$

The Hewlett-Packard machine recalls the stored numbers to its arithmetic stack and then uses reverse Polish logic (section 1.3). The T.I.58 uses algebraic logic to combine the numbers taken from the stores. The Casio machine has the simplest code; for example, the symbol 3 means 'the number in store 3'. To use 3 to mean 'the number 3' it has to be prefixed by a K, to read K3. On the other machines 3 means 'the number 3', and the $[\![RCL]\!]$ or $[\![STO]\!]$ symbols are needed to indicate that what follows is a store label number. The types of jump instruction which we mentioned in section 6.2 can be constructed with a little ingenuity on all three calculators, although the Casio probably gives the simplest versions of them, because of its simple labelling system. The T.I.58 has a flexible memory, in the sense that some of its stores can be converted to hold program steps if it is required to run a very long program. All of the three calculators can be obtained in more expensive versions which can record the program on card or magnetic strip for later use. While such facilities (and also the ability to drive a paper roll print-out attachment) are considered useful by some workers, the present author feels that such auxiliary facilities are really peripheral (and they are usually expensive). What really matters is the capacity and power of the calculator itself. It is only when the 'extras' affect this (as they do in some cases) that it is worth paying a great deal extra to get them.

6.4. Calculating π: a case study

In this section we look at a method of calculating π which goes back at least as far as Vieta (about 1600) in its algebraic form, although the geometric idea represented by the algebra goes back as far as Archimedes. The idea is that a regular polygon with n sides can be inscribed in a circle, and the perimeter of the polygon will be closer and closer in length to the circumference of the circle as n is increased. In the terminology of algebra, if we denote the perimeter by $P(n)$, and take the circle to have radius 1, so that it has circumference 2π, we have

As $n \to \infty$, Limit $P(n) = 2\pi$.

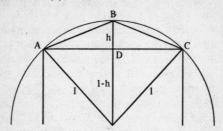

In the diagram we show a square inscribed in a circle, the side of the square being AC. Two portions of an octagon are also shown, the octagon having sides of length AB (or BC). We will denote AC by x_4 and AB by x_8, and now ask whether there is a formula which gives x_8 if we know x_4. By applying the theorem of Pythagoras to the triangle ODC, where O is the centre of the circle, we get

$$1^2 = (1-h)^2 + \tfrac{1}{4}x_4^2$$

since $(DC)^2$ is $(\tfrac{1}{2}x_4)^2$, i.e. $\tfrac{1}{4}x_4^2$.

Working out $(1-h)^2$ gives us $1 - 2h + h^2$; the 1 cancels on both sides of the equation and we obtain the result

$$\tfrac{1}{4}x_4^2 + h^2 = 2h.$$

Applying the Pythagoras theorem to triangle BCD gives

$$\tfrac{1}{4}x_4^2 + h^2 = x_8^2.$$

These last two equations take the logical form $a = b$ and $a = c$, from which we conclude $b = c$, i.e., $x_8^2 = 2h$. Here we come to a crucial point about the logical structure of the argument so far: although we started from a square ($n = 4$), the formulae would have been just the same if we had started from a polygon with any number of sides, provided that we pass to the 'bisecting' polygon with twice as many sides. Calling the side lengths x_n and x_{2n}, we arrive at the general formulae:

$$\tfrac{1}{4}x_n{}^2 + h_n{}^2 = 2h_n$$
$$\tfrac{1}{4}x_n{}^2 + h_n{}^2 = x_{2n}{}^2.$$

To be very precise (and to aid the reader's understanding) we have put a label n even on h. (Can you mark h_8 on our diagram?) As n is doubled the altitude h gets shorter, and tends to zero as n tends to infinity. We know, then, that $x_{2n}{}^2 = 2h_n$, and can now put this result into the second equation to get

$$\tfrac{1}{4}x_n{}^2 + \tfrac{1}{4}x_{2n}{}^4 = x_{2n}{}^2.$$

To find x_{2n} in terms of x_n we have to re-arrange this equation by using the same kind of trick with squares which we used in getting the algorithm for $\cos x$ in section 4.4. We start by multiplying the equation by 4, to remove the quarters, and finally obtain

$$(x_{2n}{}^2 - 2)^2 = 4 - x_n{}^2.$$

(Work it out to check that it *is* the same as the equation we started from!) Here we come to a subtle point: a calculator will always give a positive square root for a positive number, and usually no result for the square root of a negative number. When we take square roots to simplify the equation we have to take the square root of $(x_{2n}{}^2 - 2)^2$ as $(2 - x_{2n}{}^2)$, which is positive as x_{2n} tends to zero with increasing n. We find

$$x_{2n} = [2 - \surd(4 - x_n{}^2)]^{\frac{1}{2}}.$$

Starting from our geometrical picture, we have arrived at a 'translation' of our original idea into a formula involving numbers, which a calculator can handle. A calculator cannot do geometry, or work out integrals; we must convert our procedure into sequences of operations on numbers which the calculator *can* do. In this case we can see from the diagram that x_4 must equal $\sqrt{2}$, so we can set $x_4{}^2 = 2$ in the formula and get x_8, then x_{16} and so on. According to our original idea, the products $2x_4$, $4x_8$, $8x_{16}$, etc., should gradually approach π from below. We show some typical results below, and note that they 'slow down' at first as n increases, but then 'accelerate' away again at higher n values. A Texas Instruments T.I.58 calculator was used to do the calculation.

n	$\frac{1}{2}nx_n = \pi_n$	$\dfrac{\pi_{2n} - \pi_n}{\pi_{4n} - \pi_{2n}}$
16	3.136548491	4.00
32	3.140331157	4.00
64	3.141277251	4.00
128	3.141513802	4.00
256	3.141587734	3.98
512	3.141587734	3.18
1024	3.141591447	0.58

Most electronic calculators give results of the kind shown above. Mr David Kent, in an article on Vieta's method for π, quotes results (apparently obtained on a full-size computer) which 'fall back' before π is reached and gradually tend to zero. The point is that the product nx_n is of the form (large number) × (small number), so that what it does as n tends to infinity depends crucially on how the calculator handles very small numbers. For example, if x_n becomes so small that x_n^2 is registered as zero by the calculator, all later x values and all later estimates of π will come out as zero. Before this 'dead end' at high n is reached, however, most calculators pass through a region where they give *high* estimates of x_n and π because of rounding effects. The T.I.58 calculator actually settles at a limiting value of 10^{-6} for x_n, that is, does *not* yield a zero x_n if the iterations are continued. This is presumably related to the rounding procedure and the carrying of guard digits in that particular calculator, and it means that the product nx_n goes on increasing permanently as n increases.

From the table of results it can be seen that the difference of successive π estimates at first decreases, and then increases (in the region where the π estimate is too large). Indeed, the ratio of successive differences is almost exactly 4 in the low n region ($n < 256$), and if we take this as the basic 'law' of the table, which is spoiled by a rounding error at larger n values, we can calculate the theoretical 'error free' values of the π estimates. The formula needed is as follows: if the sequence of numbers a_1, a_2, a_3 ... has differences obeying the law $(a_n - a_{n-1}) = r(a_{n+1} - a_n)$, the a_n tend to the limit $a = (ra_{n+1} - a_n) \div (r-1)$, where we can choose any n value in evaluating a. For our table of π_n values we take $r = 4$ and find the estimate $\pi = 3.14159265$ from π_{64} and π_{128}. Thus, by analysing the differences we can allow fairly well for the rounding errors in this case, and the numerical table of results gave us the clue about how to correct its own defects!

Looking at our original diagram we can see that, when h is small, x_{2n} should be negligibly different from $\frac{1}{2}x_n$, so that the estimates π_{2n} and π_n are almost identical for large n (as we require). We can ensure that this stable π estimate is reached and maintained if we write the formula for x_{2n} in the form

$$x_{2n} = \tfrac{1}{2}[x_n^2 + (2 - \sqrt{4 - x_n^2})^2]^{\frac{1}{2}}.$$

When this formula is used in a T.I.58 calculator the π_n estimates tend to a stable limit of 3.141592654, which is π correct to nine decimal places. The term added to x_n^2 in the square bracket is so small at large n values that any rounding errors in it are of negligible effect on the values of x_{2n} and π_n.

Of course, the calculation of π is hardly an important problem nowadays, but our case study was intended to illustrate the following points:

1. The original calculation must be translated into a *numerical* algorithm for the calculator, and repetitive or iterative algorithms are most suitable for a programmable calculator.

2. When rounding (or other) errors affect a table of results, an analysis of the differences can often help in estimating the effect of the errors.

3. Different formulae which are *algebraically* identical may not be equally efficient for the purposes of numerical work, and a little theoretical analysis will often indicate which formula is likely to be a good one (after which, of course, the S.I.A.S. method takes over!).

6.5. Numerical integration

When a program is devised for a calculator, it is often best to present it first as a *flow-chart*, which sets out carefully what has to be done at each stage of the calculation. This chart can be followed by many readers of the program, and each reader can then translate the flow-chart into a sequence of key strokes for his individual machine.

We can do a very simple example of this, and at the same time learn a little more calculus (continuing the ideas of section 3.16).

Consider the figure below:

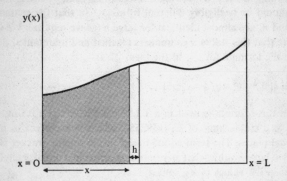

We have drawn a graph, showing how some function $y(x)$ varies with x. For example, $y(x)$ could be a polynomial in x, of the type discussed in sections 3.16 and 4.4. Consider the shaded area, which stretches from $x = 0$ up to the x value which we are considering. Clearly the size of the area will vary with the x value, so we call it $A(x)$ to remind us of this. If we shift to the right by tiny distance h, $A(x)$ will increase a little, by the amount of area in the narrow white vertical strip. This area equals (width × height), that is $hy(x)$, where $y(x)$ is the height of the strip. A careful reader will have spotted that this is not quite right, since the height of the strip varies a little as we move across it. However, if h is very small this gives a negligible error. Thus the area up to $x + h$ is given by

$$A(x + h) = A(x) + hy(x)$$

for very small h. Looking at section 3.16, you will see that this equation is precisely what we used in defining a derivative! It shows that the function $y(x)$ is the derivative of the function $A(x)$. Conversely, $A(x)$ is sometimes (loosely) called the *integral* of $y(x)$. In section 3.15 we made some comments about how, before speaking of *the* anything, we should find out whether there is only one of them. In this case we can see that, since the derivative of a constant is zero (section 3.16), we could get $y(x)$ as the derivative of $A(x)$ or $A(x)+1$ or $A(x)+1.12$, etc., so that to speak of the integral of $y(x)$ as '*the* function which has $y(x)$ as its derivative' is ambiguous unless we clearly specify a rule. For example, by applying the rule of section 2.8 for finding a derivative, we see that the polynomial

$$x^2 + 2x + 3$$

leads to the derivative $2x+2$. Applying the rule 'backwards' then gives us x^2+2x as the integral of $2x+2$, because the 3 vanished when we found the derivative. If we adapt this 'naïve' convention, then, we shall get an unambiguous integral for polynomials. However, in the case of our graph, we have a picture to guide us. We can *see* what $A(x)$ must do; it must equal zero at $x = 0$. This tells us directly which *particular* integral we need. If the function on the graph is, say, $1+x-x^2$, we would get the integral $x+\frac{1}{2}x^2-x^3$ by applying the naïve rules. This fits as it is, since it equals zero at $x = 0$. If, however, we wanted only the area between x and $\frac{1}{2}$ (not x and 0), we would have to make sure that our $A(x)$ function equals zero at $x = \frac{1}{2}$. To do this, we work out $x+\frac{1}{2}x^2-x^3$ at $x = \frac{1}{2}$, and get 0.5833 (to four figures). Accordingly the function $x+\frac{1}{2}x^2-x^3-0.5833$ will give us the area we want, and, of course, if we find its derivative we get again the result $1+x-x^2$, since the 0.5833 becomes invisible. In this way, then, we can sort out for each particular problem what we mean by *the* integral of $1+x-x^2$, or of any other function of x.

The curve $y(x)$ in the figure was drawn by hand, so we do not know what the polynomial is which fits the curve. Even when we *do* know the 'law' of $y(x)$ it may not be possible to find $A(x)$ simply by using algebra. (This often happens with the functions which are used in statistics; for example, the so-called error integral has to be looked up in numerical tables and cannot just be worked out by using a formula.) To get the area on our figure between $x = 0$ and $x = L$, we can just work it out directly by adding up the areas of lots of thin strips of width h, where h is some small number. We set out below a flow-chart to show how a programmable calculator would set about this when $y(x)$ is a *known* function for which $A(x)$ cannot be found directly using algebra. The reader should look at the chart before reading the more detailed comments

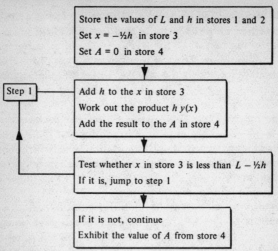

which follow it, and should refer to the previous figure if he needs further clarification.

The names L, h, x and A are for *our* benefit. It is only numbers which we put in the labelled stores. $-\frac{1}{2}h$ can be worked out to put in store 3 because we already have h in store 2. At the marked Step 1, we add h to x, which gives $x = \frac{1}{2}h$ on the first traverse of the cycle. The product $h\,y(\frac{1}{2}h)$ is then a good estimate of the area of the first strip between 0 and h. To work out $y(x)$ we need the law of $y(x)$, so this part of the program may be quite lengthy and will depend on the particular $y(x)$ function. Adding the area of the strip into store 4 gives us the total area so far. If x is less than L, we must move to the middle of the next strip and add its area into the total. This is what the jump achieves, but when we get up to $L-\frac{1}{2}h$ (the middle of the last strip) the jump does not occur; instead we simply get the total area displayed. Of course, h cannot be *any* small number; it must be such that a whole number of strips fit into the length L. When the area has been calculated, it can be calculated again using a smaller h, just to check that the strips were narrow enough to give a good estimate.

As an example of the ideas of this section we consider the evaluation of the area A between $x = 0$ and $x = 1$ for the case in which $y(x)$ equals $\exp(-x^2)$. (The exponential function was treated in section 4.6.) The traditional notation for this area is

$$A = \int_0^1 \exp(-x^2).dx$$

and the process of working out A is called *integration*. $\int$ is the *integral sign*, and in general the upper and lower numbers on the integral sign give us the x values between which we are working out the area (or integral). We can try using the power series for $\exp(-x^2)$, that is, we use $-x^2$ in place of x in the series which we discussed in section 4.6. We know how to deal with powers of x, and we proceed as follows. First, we replace $\exp(-x^2)$ by its power series:

$$A = \int_0^1 [1 - x^2 + \tfrac{1}{2}x^4 - \tfrac{1}{6}x^6 + \tfrac{1}{24}x^8 \ldots]dx.$$

Then we integrate each term and take the effect of the series:

$$A = [x - \tfrac{1}{3}x^3 + \tfrac{1}{10}x^5 - \tfrac{1}{42}x^7 + \tfrac{1}{216}x^9 \ldots]_0^1.$$

The reader may check that the power series in this last equation correctly gives the $\exp(-x^2)$ series as its derivative. Since the power series equals zero at $x = 0$, we only need to work out its value at $x = 1$ to get the area between 0 and 1. Setting $x = 1$, and taking more and more terms, we find that we have to go up to the x^{21} term before the resulting sum 'settles down' (converges) to seven decimal places, giving $A = 0.7468241$. In many cases this power series approach does not give a convergent process, and we must rely entirely on the numerical approach, for which we gave the flow-chart previously. Using that flow-chart (on a Casio fx201P calculator) for our calculation actually gave values of A as follows (with the strip width in a bracket); we used three strip widths, in the ratio 4:2:1.

(0.05)	0.7469008	$A(4h)$
(0.025)	0.7468433	$A(2h)$
(0.0125)	0.7468289	$A(h)$

More advanced theory suggests that the numerical method gives an error in the area which varies as h^2 when h is small. We can check this empirically as follows. If we use strip widths, h, $2h$ and $4h$, as we did to get the quoted numbers, we ought to have

$$\frac{A(4h) - A(2h)}{A(2h) - A(h)} = \frac{(4h)^2 - (2h)^2}{(2h)^2 - h^2} = 4.$$

In fact we find that this ratio is 3.993 for our results, in good agreement with an h^2 dependence of the error. This being so, we can find out what the true value of A is, since the h^2 law will also give the relation

$$A(2h) - A = 4[A(h) - A].$$

This gives us the result (upon solving this equation to find A)

$$A = \tfrac{1}{3}[4A(h) - A(2h)]$$

which gives us $A = 0.746824$ from our results above, and agrees with the result from the power series approach.

6.6. Roots of equations. Newton's method

Suppose that we wish to find a root of the equation

$$x^3 + 2x^2 - 2x - 3 = 0$$

that is, an x value for which the polynomial on the left adds up to zero. We find, by simply trying out a few values, that for $x = 1$ the polynomial equals -2, while for $x = 2$ it equals 9. This suggests that a root lies between $x = 1$ and $x = 2$. Now, suppose we call the polynomial $F(x)$ for short, and also we call its derivative (which in this case is $3x^2 + 4x - 2$) $G(x)$ for short. If we use an x value which is close to the root X, we can set $X = x + h$, with h small. From our definition of a derivative (section 3.16) we see that the value of $F(x)$ at $x = X$ will be

$$F(x + h) = F(x) + hG(x) + \text{tiny corrections}$$
$$= 0$$

since $F(X)$ is zero; we know this, since X is a root of the equation. We thus find

$$X = x + h$$
$$= x - \frac{F(x)}{G(x)}.$$

This is not exact, because of the tiny correction terms, but the right-hand side depends entirely on x. We thus get an iterative process, of the kind encountered previously. For our particular choice of $F(x)$ the right-hand side is

$$x - \frac{(x^3 + 2x^2 - 2x - 3)}{(3x^2 + 4x - 2)}.$$

We put $x = 1$ into this, to get x_1, which we put in again to get x_2, etc. We get the following results: 1, 1.4, 1.3088608, 1.3027757, 1.3027757... using a Sinclair Enterprise calculator. Thus the iterative process converges to give a root of the equation. Clearly, this process is ideal for a programmable calculator, since it could easily deal with any coefficients: we could write a program to deal with $Ax^3 + Bx^2 + Cx + D$ instead of $x^3 + 2x^2 - 2x - 3$, and put A, B, C, D into four of the stores when starting off the execution of the program. We would have to put our first guess x_0 into another store, into which x_1 would go when calculated. If our guess x_0 were too inaccurate, the process might not converge, or it might converge to a root remote from the one which we intended to find. For example, if we set x_0 equal to 1, 2, 50, or 400 we still get 1.3027757 as the root in our specimen problem, but setting $x_0 = 0$ leads to -1 (a second root), while setting $x_0 = -2$ leads to -2.3027757 (a third root). Indeed there are theorems from the theory of equations which say that the cubic equation should have three roots, and that they should add up to $-1 \times$ (coefficient of $x^2 \div$ coefficient of x^3), which is -2 for our specimen equation. We found three real roots, but for some choices of (real) A, B, C, D, only one of the roots of a cubic equation is real, while the other two are complex numbers, of the type discussed in section 3.15. On modern programmable calculators it is possible to devise programs to get the roots even when they are complex numbers.

The (British) Sinclair Enterprise calculator, which was used to treat the above example, is one of the lowest priced and physically compact programmable calculators currently available. It has an 80-step program memory, with the useful feature that a HALT instruction is permanently stored at the 00 step of any program and so need not be inserted explicitly; the calculator proceeds up to step 79 and then returns to 00 and halts (unless, of course, extra loops are used to make it jump to some other step and continue the calculation). The Enterprise has seven data stores, and has the novel feature of an automatic K constant (which is missing on almost all scientific and programmable calculators) and also an $X - Y$ exchange key, which is relatively rare on algebraic logic scientific calculators. Numbers can be moved into and out of the stores without destroying the stored K constant operation. The calculator will fit nicely into an inside pocket of a jacket, and is useful for doing calculations on journeys (apart from the obvious slight problem with airport metal detector equipment!).

6.7. Matrix inverses. Linear equations

Consider the pair of simultaneous equations:

$$ax + by = \alpha$$
$$cx + dy = \beta$$

for which we know α and β (and a, b, c, d) but require x and y. If we use the matrix ideas of section 4.14, we can write our pair of equations as one matrix equation:

$$M\underline{x} = \underline{\alpha}$$

where M is a 2×2 matrix, and $\underline{x}$ and $\underline{\alpha}$ are columns of two numbers ($\underline{x}$ has the elements x and y and $\underline{\alpha}$ has the elements α and β.) If we had an equation $Mx = \alpha$ involving *numbers*, we would simply put $x = M^{-1}\alpha$ to find x, with M^{-1} being the reciprocal of M. Now, one of the beauties of the matrix notation is that the *same solution holds for a matrix equation*, if M^{-1} is the inverse matrix of M, i.e., the matrix such that $MM^{-1} = 1$, the unit matrix. (All of these ideas have already been encountered in Chapter 4.) We can write down the solution as

$$\underline{x} = M^{-1}\underline{\alpha}$$

and in this general matrix version it no longer matters whether there are two, three or more simultaneous equations. We can solve the equations if we can find M^{-1}, the inverse matrix. For example, we can easily spot the solution for our 2×2 case:

$$\begin{pmatrix} a & b \\ c & d \end{pmatrix}^{-1} = \frac{1}{(ad-bc)}\begin{pmatrix} d & -b \\ -c & a \end{pmatrix}$$

(Remember S.I.A.S.; work it out and *show* that $MM^{-1} = I$, the unit 2×2 matrix.)

For larger matrices it is not so easy to remember the formulae for the elements of M^{-1} and so a numerical calculation is often easier if we are given the elements of M as numbers. Here again, an interesting thing happens. If we wanted M^{-1} for a *number* M, we have seen (section 4.14) that the formula

$$x = x(2 - Mx)$$

used in an iterative calculation, will lead to M^{-1}. *The same is true for matrices*, if we use matrix multiplications throughout and start from some initial matrix guess x_0 for M^{-1}. 2 is replaced by $2I$, where I is the unit matrix. If we make a very bad first guess the process will not converge, and we must try again.

If we find M^{-1}, we can find the solution $\underline{x}$ for *any* input $\underline{\alpha}$. However, for a particular $\underline{\alpha}$, it is possible to find $\underline{x}$ without constructing the full inverse matrix M^{-1}.

For example consider the problem:

$$\begin{pmatrix} 6 & 2 & 1 \\ 2 & 2 & 1 \\ 1 & 2 & 5 \end{pmatrix}\begin{pmatrix} x \\ y \\ z \end{pmatrix} = \begin{pmatrix} 3 \\ 2 \\ 1 \end{pmatrix}$$

We can write this as a set of equations:

$$x = \tfrac{1}{6}(3 - 2y - z)$$
$$y = \tfrac{1}{2}(2 - 2x - z)$$
$$z = \tfrac{1}{5}(1 - x - 2y)$$

and, starting from some guess for y and z, say $y = z = 0$, keep on working out x, y, z in an iterative manner. A very simple program will do this, and we can arrange for it to display z, say, after each circuit of the three equations. Starting from $y = z = 0$ we find for our specimen problem,

$$x = 0.25, \quad y = 0.6964285714, \quad z = 0.1071428571.$$

The method described above is the *Gauss-Seidel* method, and it works provided that the elements along the diagonal of the matrix (i.e. the numbers 6, 2, 5 for our example) are sufficiently large compared to the other elements. Many of the matrices arising in scientific problems are *symmetric*, i.e. have their elements M_{ij} and M_{ji} equal. (Our specimen matrix is *not* symmetric, because it has $M_{23} = 1$ but $M_{32} = 2$.)

Exercises

1. Consider the simply polynomial function

$$y(x) = x - x^2.$$

Draw a graph of this between $x = 0$ and $x = 1$. Find the area under the curve between these end points. Show that at $x = \frac{1}{2}$ the function $y(x)$ has a maximum value of $\frac{1}{4}$, and that a rectangle of this height and of length 1 has an area $\frac{3}{2}$ times that under the curve (which is a parabola).

Solution

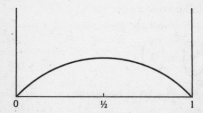

We remember that the area $A(x)$ between 0 and x has the derivative $x - x^2$, which gives $\frac{1}{2}x^2 - \frac{1}{3}x^3$ as $A(x)$; this correctly equals 0 at $x = 0$ and equals $\frac{1}{6}$ at $x = 1$. The derivative of $x - x^2$ equals $1 - 2x$, and is zero at $x = \frac{1}{2}$; at this point $x - x^2$ equals $\frac{1}{4}$.

2. Suppose that a programmable calculator is required to jump to some previous step when the number in some store X either exceeds 1 or is less than 0. If the calculator can only be instructed to jump if the contents of some specific store T are negative, how can we accomplish the required jump?

Solution

We use x to denote the number in store X. We work out $x(1-x)$ and put this in store T. If x is greater than 1 or less than 0 the number $x(1-x)$ will be less than 0 and the jump will be accomplished. The function concerned is that already used in problem 1. Our T store jump condition is a simplified version of one used on some Texas Instruments machines, and also appears in the Sinclair Enterprise.

3. A programmable calculator may have to perform thousands of calculations in the course of executing a long program. If there are any rounding errors, it is in such long calculations that they may affect the results, particularly if the result of an early stage of the calculation is used as an input at a later stage. Some companies (e.g. Texas Instruments and Hewlett-Packard) make programmable calculators which exhibit (say) nine figures in the display, but calculate internally with (say) twelve figures. The extra hidden 'guard digits' make it very unlikely that the displayed result is affected by rounding error. How could you check that a calculator does have these guard digits?

Solution

We can see them as follows (for the particular case of the T.I.58). We evaluate $\sqrt{2}$, to make sure that all twelve digits will be activated. The display shows 1.414213562, which we write down. We then *subtract* this from $\sqrt{2}$ on the calculator. We see 4×10^{-10} displayed (not zero). Further subtracting 4×10^{-10} from this gives -2.7×10^{-11}. Adding 2.7×10^{-11} gives zero. We see that inside the calculator we had for $\sqrt{2}$ the value

$$1.414213562 + 10^{-12}(400 - 27) = 1.414213562373.$$

(Compare this with the result obtained in section 3.6.)

4. Treat the equation

$$x^2 - 2 = 0$$

by the method of section 6.6. Show that the resulting equation for the iterative process is the same as that found by other arguments in section 3.4.

Solution

We have

$$F(x) = x^2 - 2$$
$$G(x) = 2x.$$

Thus we need to evaluate

$$x - \frac{F(x)}{G(x)}$$

$$= x - \frac{(x^2 - 2)}{2x}$$

$$= \tfrac{1}{2}x + \frac{2}{x}.$$

This average of x and $2/x$ is what was used in section 3.4.

5. Try the matrix inverse calculation of section 6.7, but interchange the 6 and the 2 in the first row. What happens? Can you still get the solution?

Does the Gauss-Seidel method (when it works) allow us to find M^{-1}, i.e. the full inverse matrix?

Solution

The numbers get bigger and bigger, i.e. the process diverges. However, it works properly if we use the first row to give the equation *for y* (not x) and the second row to give the equation for x (since we already have one for y). The trick is to make sure that the large coefficient (6 in this case) is used to divide in the equation. If the Gauss-Seidel method is applied with α chosen to be a column with one element equal to 1 and the others equal to 0, then the solution x is one column of the inverse matrix M^{-1}. By varying the position of the 1, we can get every column in M^{-1}.

6. Show that if we use Newton's method (section 6.6) to find the real roots of a polynomial equation of form

$$0 = A_0 + A_1 x + A_2 x^2 + \ldots + A_n x^n = F(x)$$

then the resulting iterative formula for x can be written as

$$x = P(x) \div Q(x)$$

where P and Q are polynomials and P has no x term in it.

Solution

The text shows that we have to work out $x - F(x)/G(x)$, where $G(x)$ is the derivative of $F(x)$. We can write the result as $[xG(x) - F(x)]/G(x)$, so that it is a ratio of polynomials. Since $A_1 x$ has the derivative A_1, the x terms in $[xG - F]$ cancel exactly. The result is

$$x = \frac{-A_0 + A_2 x^2 + 2A_3 x^3 + \ldots}{A_1 + 2A_2 x + 3A_3 x^2 + \ldots}$$

and it is easy to write a program which works this out if A_0, A_1, A_2, etc. are the input, together with an initial guess x_0. We note that Newton's method involves division, whereas our iterative formula for the inverse X^{-1} (section 4.14) has the feature that it uses only multiplication and subtraction. The X^{-1} formula *can* be obtained from Newton's method by studying the equation $1 - X^{-1}x^{-1} = 0$. (Try it!)

Postscript

This book was primarily intended to influence ideas about the learning and teaching of mathematics in English-speaking countries. It seems, however, that the use of calculators in education has already been encouraged in some other countries. For example, in Denmark around 50,000 calculators are bought by the education authorities each year for use in secondary schools, and are provided free for the pupils. This mass usage apparently showed that the fairly rough treatment involved led to errors developing in 15,000 out of 110,000 low-priced calculators during one year. Obviously, then, there is still a need for the development of very simple and robust calculators; it may be that the keyless kind of machine mentioned in Chapter 1 will be useful in this regard.

It has recently been suggested that work on new transistor and memory materials may eventually make it possible for computer arithmetic units to work ten or a hundred times faster than they do at present. If such developments should spread to the programmable calculator field, they would represent a valuable advance. In the author's opinion, such an advance would be of much more value than the current tendency to add more and more peripheral facilities to calculators.

All the methods used in this book would, of course, work on a mechanical calculator, although they would be very laborious and the extra work would not lead to extra understanding. We must regretfully note that, when this book was started (late 1978), such laborious procedures *were* having to be used by certain able educationalists in Israel. Apparently the programmable electronic calculator was classed as a luxury article under import regulations; the resulting import duty made sure that it *was* a luxury article! We trust that the absurdity of such an obstacle to efficient education is clear enough not to need further emphasis here. (We are glad to note that the duty has now been reduced.)

In the past few years various experiments have been carried out on the use of calculators in schools and these have been described in reports by, for example, the School Mathematics Project, the County of Durham Education Committee and the Shell Centre for Mathematical Education at the University of Nottingham. These reports contain a few interesting 'psychological' observations: some teachers noted that shy children, who were usually slow to admit errors to the teacher, were quite happy to go check their own hand calculations on an 'impersonal' calculator; one teacher commented that a 'press and see' approach to simple arithmetic had been effective in teaching an immigrant child who could not yet converse properly in spoken English. Many schoolchildren nowadays receive some kind of course in computing: the Oxfordshire Education Authority has recently obtained a second-hand computer to be set up for teaching purposes in one of its schools. However, it is important to remember that *computing* is an art thousands of years old, if we think of it as the devising of efficient ways of calculating; the skills involved in computing in this older sense can be acquired more cheaply by the use of small electronic calculators.

Programmable calculators now seem to be developing in two directions. Some calculators (e.g. the C.B.M. Statistician) have many pre-programmed operations built into them for special calculations, so that they provide great power in dealing with particular financial or statistical calculations; others (e.g. the T.I.58) have 'plug-in' modules with specialized programs, while also allowing the operator to write his own new programs. For educational and research work, the second type is clearly more flexible. Certain developments in programmable calculator design necessarily go 'hand in hand'; for example, if program lengths increase, the number of digits used by the machine will have to do so as well if rounding errors are to be kept under control, since the increased program length will allow many more operations (each with a rounding error) to be carried out during a calculation.

Appendix 1
Useful Numbers

$$e = 2.718281828$$
$$\pi = 3.14159265$$

1 kilogram = 2.2046 pounds $\left.\right\}$ see exercise 3
    1 litre = 0.2200 gallons $\left.\right\}$ of Chapter 1
    1 inch = 2.54 centimetres
    1 mile = 1.6093 kilometres
  (5 miles $\simeq$ 8 kilometres)

Appendix 2
Formulae for Trigonometric Functions

$\cos x = \frac{1}{24}[(x^2 - 6)^2 - 12]$

x must be in radians. For $x < 0.3$, the error is less than 10^{-6}. For larger x the angle doubling formula

$\cos 2x = 2\cos^2 x - 1$

can be used. $\sin x$ and $\tan x$ follow from $\cos x$, but we give alternative formulae for them

$\sin x = \frac{x}{120}[(x^2 - 10)^2 + 20]$.

For $x < 0.5$ the error is less than 10^{-6}. The result $\sin x = \cos(\pi/2 - x)$ is useful.

$\tan x = \frac{x}{120}[(4x^2 + 5)^2 + 95]$.

For $x < 0.2$ the error is less than 10^{-6}. $\tan x$ is very large for angles near $\pi/2$, and the following formulae are helpful in that region,

$\tan(\pi/2 - x) = \frac{1}{\tan x}$

$\tan 2x = \frac{2\tan x}{1 - \tan^2 x}$

Appendix 3

Formulae for cosh x, e^x, ln x

$\cosh x = \frac{1}{24}[(x^2+6)^2-12]$.

For $x < 0.3$ the error is less than 10^{-6}. For larger x the doubling formula

$\cosh 2x = 2\cosh^2 x - 1$

can be used.

There are various formulae for e^x; one which is easy to remember is

$$e^x = \frac{(x+3)^2+3}{(x-3)^2+3}.$$

The error is less than 10^{-6} for $x < 0.25$. Knowing e, it is not necessary to find e^x for an x value greater than this, since $e^{\frac{1}{2}}$, $e^{\frac{1}{4}}$ can be found by using the square root key (e.g. $e^{0.721} = e^{0.5} \times e^{0.221}$). If we do wish to find e^x for larger x without a square root key, we use the law of indices, e.g.

$e^{0.721} = (e^{0.18025})^4$.

A simple formula for ln x is

$$\ln x = \frac{3(x^2-1)}{(x+2)^2-3}.$$

The error is less than 10^{-6} for $0.8 < x < 1.2$. For larger x we take the square root n times to get down to about 1.1, find the log, then multiply it by 2^n.

(Section 4.10 of Chapter 4 gives some alternative formulae for e^x.)

Appendix 4
Formula for x^y

Take the square root of x (n times) to get down to a number x_0, which lies between 1.001 and 1.002. Work out $(x_0 - 1)y + 1$, and then square this result n times to get x^y. The error depends on x and y, but is usually less than a tenth of one per cent.

Appendix 5
Formula for $\cos^{-1}x$

$$\cos^{-1}x = [-(24x+12)^{\frac{1}{2}}+6]^{\frac{1}{2}}$$

Error less than 10^{-5} radian for $1 > x > 0.92$.

For smaller x, use the reduction formula

$$\cos\tfrac{x}{2} = [\tfrac{1}{2}(1+\cos x)]^{\frac{1}{2}}$$

Some Further Reading

We describe here some works which readers will find useful if they wish to learn more about the use of calculators in specific tasks. Students of science will find much material in two articles by the present author. *Contemporary Physics*, Vol. 17, page 145 (1976) and Vol. 18, page 265 (1977). The first article deals with simple calculators while the second deals with programmable calculators. Below we list some books which deal with calculators.

1. *The Electronic Calculator in Business, Home and School* by C. Birtwistle (Elliott Right Way Books)
This is an interesting low-priced easy-to-read paperback which has much in it about money calculations, calculations of areas and volumes, metric conversions, etc. The book deals only with the older arithmetic logic and with simple algebraic logic (whereas A.O.S. algebraic and reverse Polish logics are also explained in the present book). It gives metric conversion factors to high accuracy (e.g. 1 inch = 2.5399999 centimetres). In the present author's opinion this accuracy is too great for everyday use, besides making the factors hard to remember. (See exercise 3, Chapter 1, in the present book.) It seems that some of the book's discussion of accuracy is misleading. Thus, in Chapter 13 it is stated (correctly) that a rectangle of 7.3 metres by 4.8 metres gives an area of 35.04 square metres. However, it is not true to imply (as the book does) that, if the lengths are correct to decimetres, the area is correct to *square* decimetres. For example, if we take the lengths to be 7.35 metres and 4.85 metres we get an area of 35.65 square metres. This represents an uncertainty of ± 61 square decimetres (not 1 square decimetre) if we follow the convention that 7.3 means 'between 7.25 and 7.35'.

2. *The Pocket Calculator Pocket Book* by R. J. Goult and M. J. Pratt (Stanley Thornes (Publishers) Ltd)
This is a useful cheap paperback which, besides dealing with money calculations and metric conversions, also treats square and cube roots, simple polynomials, simple statistical calculations and trigonometric functions. In

dealing with $\cos x$, $\cosh x$, etc., the book uses rather unwieldy formulae, with 'awkward' coefficients, whereas we have used the squaring process and angle doubling to give more simple formulae in the present book.

3. *Advanced Applications for Pocket Calculators* by J. Gilbert (Foulsham-Tab Ltd)

This paperback describes a wide range of scientific calculations and gives details of many specific calculators. An interesting feature is a 'stretching' process (analogous to that of section 3.6 in the present book) which enables very large numbers to be multiplied on an eight-figure calculator. The theory of the square root and cube root iterative calculations is explained in detail, although the generalization to nth roots is not noted. Gilbert's book does what many other books on numerical methods do: it quotes different formulae for different x regions (for $\cos x$, $\sin x$, etc.). We think it preferable to have one basic formula and use angle doubling. Also, we regard it as part of the purpose of a calculator algorithm to *avoid* the use of tables, whereas some of Gilbert's calculations use the calculator essentially as an interpolating device which needs tables of $\cos x$, $\sin x$, etc.

4. *Scientific Analysis on the Pocket Calculator* by J. M. Smith (John Wiley)

This is an advanced and expensive book intended for serious scientific workers, and includes a great variety of material on statistical problems, matrix problems, numerical integrations, Fourier analysis, Chebysev polynomials, determination of roots of polynomials, etc. Our only major criticism of it is that some of the formulae given for simple functions such as $\cos x$ involve complicated coefficients which are almost impossible to remember, whereas the present book gives formulae with simple integer coefficients which are easy to remember. As a minor point, we note that Smith says that there does not seem to be an easy way of working out a product of sums on a calculator without a memory. It *can* be done, as follows,

$$(a+b)(c+d) = \left[(a+b)\frac{c}{d} + a + b \right] d.$$

(After comments from the present author – and others – Smith's second edition deals with this point.)

5. *Applied Mathematical Physics with Programmable Pocket Calculators* by R. M. Eisberg (McGraw-Hill)

This is a university undergraduate paperback which shows how programmable calculators can be used to deal with numerical integration, oscillating systems, and a variety of problems both in classical and quantum mechanics. The principal theme of the book is that numerical methods for dealing with differential equations are (1) easy to understand, (2) essentially the same for equations which need *different* analytical approaches and (3) give useful results even for some problems where analytical methods will not work. The book gives typical programs for an algebraic logic calculator and a reverse Polish logic calculator, and certainly will help students of mechanics to get a good feel for the computational aspects of the subject. (The present author also has an interest in the use of calculators in quantum mechanics, and the second of the *Contemporary Physics* articles mentioned earlier deals with the topic.)

6. *Algorithms for R P N Calculators* by J. A. Ball (Wiley – Interscience)
This is an expensive hardback, likely to appeal mainly to scientists, and giving many details about the use of calculators which employ reverse Polish logic. The book clearly champions reverse Polish logic as being superior to algebraic logic (although many scientists remain unconvinced). The present author has one slight criticism of the tables of identities (e.g. $\sqrt{x^2} = x$) which Ball presents: two *algebraically* identical expressions may not be equivalent when used on a calculator, because of rounding errors or because of the differing number of key strokes which they involve. The present book makes this point repeatedly, while Ball does not seem to emphasize it sufficiently. (See, for example, exercise 3 of Chapter 3 in the present book.)

7. *Arithmetic and Calculators* by W. G. Chinn, R. A. Dean and T. N. Tracewell (W. H. Freeman)
In my Introduction I exhort teachers to make maximum use of high-speed calculators when teaching basic mathematical skills. I am pleased to discover that this book carries out splendidly part of the programme which I advocate. It should be a standard item in the library of every school which takes seriously the teaching of basic mathematical skills. I have only one criticism: on page 15, where the authors introduce the use of brackets in calculations, they miss the opportunity to explain the difference between S.A.L. and A.O.S. calculators and to point out that some calculators have bracket keys. This knowledge, of course, would be useful to a teacher about to set up a 'calculator arithmetic' course. However, that criticism aside, the book gives the reader a thorough grounding in arithmetic, with lots of worked examples (many of them exhibiting the key strokes involved). The arithmetic of decimal numbers is carefully explained, and general notions such as those of commutativity and distributivity are skilfully and

gently introduced. Areas, percentages, interest, square and cube roots and other 'everyday arithmetic' topics are treated in detail. The mark of a creative author (or teacher) is that he can treat his subject without arrogance, leaving himself and his reader open to the discovery of new fascination and insight in the study of simple 'basic' material. To find an author with this ability is pleasant: to find three is a delight.

Many of the methods used in this book will work on microcomputers such as the Pet, the Apple, and the ZX 81. The present author's book *Microcomputer Quantum Mechanics* (Adam Hilger) will appear during 1982 and should be useful to students of physics and mathematics.

Index